Developing Fluency: Dividing by 1-Digit Divisors

Common Core

Standards for Mathematical Content

Domain Number and Operations in Base Ten

Cluster Use place value understanding and properties of operations to perform multi-digit arithmetic.

Cluster Generalize place value understanding for multi-digit whole numbers.

Standards 4.NBT.6, Also 4.NBT.1, 4.NBT.5, 4.OA.3

Standards for Mathematical Practice

✔ Make sense of problems and persevere in solving them.

✔ Reason abstractly and quantitatively.

✔ Construct viable arguments and critique the reasoning of others.

✔ Model with mathematics.

✔ Use appropriate tools strategically.

✔ Attend to precision.

✔ Look for and make use of structure.

✔ Look for and express regularity in repeated reasoning.

D1315214

Copyright © 2012 by Pearson Education, Inc., or its affiliates. All Rights Reserved. Printed in the United States of America. This publication is protected by copyright, and permission should be obtained from the publisher prior to any prohibited reproduction, storage in a retrieval system, or transmission in any form or by any means, electronic, mechanical, photocopying, recording, or likewise. For information regarding permissions, write to Rights Management & Contracts, Pearson Education, Inc., One Lake Street, Upper Saddle River, New Jersey 07458.

Pearson, Scott Foresman, Pearson Scott Foresman, and enVisionMATH are trademarks, in the U.S. and/or in other countries, of Pearson Education Inc., or its affiliates.

Common Core State Standards: © Copyright 2010. National Governors Association Center for Best Practices and Council of Chief State School Officers. All rights reserved.

UNDERSTANDING BY DESIGN® and UbD™ are trademarks of the Association for Supervision and Curriculum Development (ASCD), and are used under license.

ISBN-13: 978-0-328-67396-4
ISBN-10: 0-328-67396-X

6 7 8 9 10 V064 15 14 13 12

BIG IDEA Operation Meanings & Relationships There are multiple interpretations of addition, subtraction, multiplication, and division of rational numbers, and each operation is related to other operations.

ESSENTIAL UNDERSTANDING

10-1   Repeated subtraction situations can be modeled and solved using division.

BIG IDEA Algorithms There is more than one algorithm for each of the operations with rational numbers. Most algorithms for operations with rational numbers, both mental math and paper and pencil, use equivalence to transform calculations into simpler ones.

ESSENTIAL UNDERSTANDINGS

10-2   Repeated subtraction situations can be solved using a division algorithm different from the standard algorithm.

10-3   The sharing interpretation of division can be used to model the standard division algorithm.

10-4, 10-5, 10-7   The standard division algorithm breaks the calculation into simpler calculations using basic facts, place value, the relationship between multiplication and division, and estimation.

BIG IDEA Estimation Numbers can be approximated by numbers that are close. Numerical calculations can be approximated by replacing numbers with other numbers that are close and easy to compute mentally.

ESSENTIAL UNDERSTANDING

10-6   The relationship between multiplication, division, and estimation can help determine the place value of the largest digit in a quotient.

BIG IDEA Practices, Processes, and Proficiencies Mathematics content and practices can be applied to solve problems.

ESSENTIAL UNDERSTANDING

10-8   Some problems can be solved by first finding and solving a sub-problem(s) and then using that answer(s) to solve the original problem.

Repeated Subtraction

When relating division to repeated subtraction, the amount in each group is known and the number of equal groups needs to be determined. This is also referred to as "measurement division," in which groups of equal size are measured off from the whole. Consider the following problem:

> Muriel has 20 photo albums. She can pack 4 albums in each storage box. How many boxes does she need to store all of her albums?

One way to solve this problem and find the number of boxes, or equal groups, is to subtract groups of 4 from 20 until zero is reached.

$$
\begin{array}{r}
20 \\
-4 \\
\hline
16 \\
-4 \\
\hline
12 \\
-4 \\
\hline
8 \\
-4 \\
\hline
4 \\
-4 \\
\hline
0 \\
\end{array}
$$

There are 5 groups of 4 that can be subtracted from 20. Muriel needs 5 boxes to store all of her albums.

This problem can also be represented by a bar diagram that shows what is known (the whole amount and the amount in each group) and what needs to be determined (the number of equal groups). Because the number of groups is unknown, it is only possible to show one section of the bar.

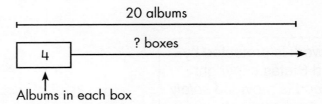

Albums in each box

Another representation of this problem is the equation $20 \div 4 = 5$, in which the dividend is the whole amount, the divisor is the number in each group, and the quotient is the number of equal groups.

The Division Algorithm

Language of Division

The way in which you describe division is related to the approach you are using. If you were to divide 98 by 4 using repeated subtraction you might start by saying, "How many 4s are in 98?" or, "Four goes into 98 how many times?" The language of the sharing model is different. To divide 98 by 4 you would say, "9 tens are divided into 4 groups. How many go in each group?" The example below shows how to explain all the steps of the algorithm for dividing 98 by 4.

Step 1: Divide the tens.

Think: 9 tens divided into 4 groups
How many tens in each group?

```
   2
4)98
 − 8↓
  18
```

- 2 tens in each group
- 8 tens shared altogether
- 1 ten left over
- Trade 1 ten for 10 ones
- Bring down 8 ones. 10 ones and 8 ones is 18 ones.

Step 2: Divide the ones.

Think: 18 ones divided into 4 groups
How many ones in each group?

```
  24 R2
4)98
 − 8↓
  18
 −16
   2
```

- 4 ones in each group
- 16 ones shared altogether
- 2 ones left over

Mathematical Practices: Use Appropriate Tools

If students have difficulty with the algorithm for dividing, allow them to use place-value blocks to model each step. This will help them connect the concrete actions to each symbolic step.

Special Considerations

Zeros and Regrouping

When using the sharing method of division, there are times when there is not enough in a place value to divide equally into the necessary number of groups. In this case, it is important that students place a zero in the quotient to indicate that the particular place value cannot be divided. Instead, the number in that place value will be regrouped and added to the next place value to be divided.

For example, when dividing 314 by 3, the quotient should be 104 R2, not 14 R2. Again, drawing lines to delineate place values or having students work on grid paper may help them remember to record the appropriate digits.

Placing the First Digit

In some cases, there may not be enough in the leading place value of the dividend to divide into equal groups. For example, when dividing 678 by 8, you cannot divide 6 hundreds into 8 groups. So, the 6 hundreds are regrouped as 60 tens and added to the 7 tens to get 67 tens, which can be divided into 8 groups. It is vital to make sure students write the first digit of the quotient in the tens place rather than the hundreds place, as there were no hundreds to divide. If students have trouble remembering this, you can either have them write a 0 in the hundreds place, or have them draw lines to show the place values in the dividend and the quotient.

```
   08              H│T│O
8)678      or        │8│
 −64            8)6│7│8
                 −6│4│
```

Mathematical Practices: Check for Reasonableness

Have students estimate before dividing. This will tell them how many digits will be in the quotient and can help prevent errors involving zeros.

For a complete list of *enVisionMATH* Professional Development resources in print, on DVD, and online, see the *Teacher's Program Overview*.

225B

 INTERVENTION

ELL

Considerations for ELL Students

Repeated oral language practice of the terms that are used in the division algorithms will help English learners remember and understand the steps.

- **Beginning** Display the problem $34 \div 8 = 4\ R2$ on the board. Have students copy the problem and label its parts with the terms *quotient*, *dividend*, *divisor*, and *remainder*. Have pairs of students compare their labeling, talking through any discrepancies.

- **Intermediate** Display a division pattern and have students point out the *basic fact*, *divisor*, *dividend*, and *quotient* for each number sentence. Have students create sentences to describe the division algorithm, such as: *There are 21 tens in the dividend. When this is divided by 7, there are 3 tens in the quotient.*

- **Advanced** Assign each group a divisor from 2 to 9. Have groups use counters to model and record division exercises using their divisor and the dividends 12 through 20. Have students discuss each problem, quotient, and remainder using proper terminology. Have groups compare the size of the remainder and the divisor.

Special Needs

Considerations for Special Needs Students

- Review with special needs students the value of one ten rod and then the value of a group of tens rods. Have students create statements such as: *2 tens rods is 20.*

- Repeat with hundreds flats.

Below Level

Considerations for Below-Level Students

- Comprehending the meaning of the numbers in the division algorithm is important for students to be able to divide.

- Provide students who are performing below level with practice using manipulatives, such as counters.

Advanced/Gifted

Considerations for Advanced/Gifted Students

- Students who gain quick understanding of dividing with remainders can practice writing stories that include this kind of division.

- Discuss with students types of problems when the remainder should be ignored and types of problems when the remainder is the answer.

Response to Intervention

 Ongoing Intervention
- Lessons with guiding questions to assess understanding
- Support to prevent misconceptions and to reteach

 Strategic Intervention
- Targeted to small groups who need more support
- Easy to implement

 Intensive Intervention
- Instruction to accelerate progress
- Instruction focused on foundational skills

Reading Comprehension and Problem Solving

Ⓒ **Use Structure: Use Reading Comprehension Strategies**

A good reading comprehension strategy to use in math is to *note important information in the text (identify the main idea)*.

Questions to Guide Comprehension

Use these questions to guide comprehension of the problem before students give the answer to the problem.

Lesson 10-5, Exercise 18

1 *What do you need to find? Circle that in the problem.* [How many cars did it take each hour?]

2 *What do you know? Underline that in the problem.* [The ferry transported a total of 685 cars over a 5-hour period. The ferry took the same number of cars each hour.]

3 *Is there any extra information? Cross that out in the problem.* [Cross out the first sentence: The Galveston-Port Bolivar Ferry takes cars across Galveston Bay.]

4 *How can you show the problem? Make a drawing.* [Sample drawing shown at the right.]

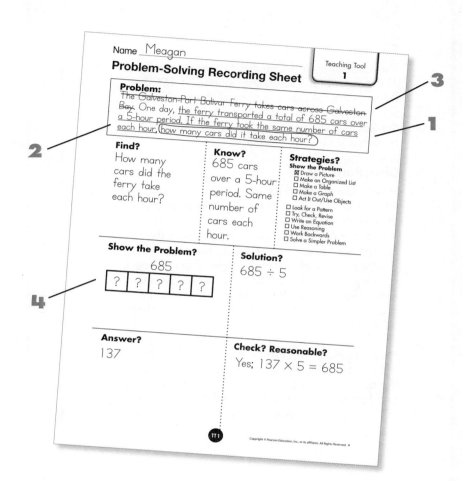

Vocabulary Activities

Dividing 2-Digit Numbers

Ⓒ **Attend to Precision** Write a division problem on the board, such as 58 ÷ 4. Ask students to estimate the answer. Then have them solve the problem and explain how they solved it.

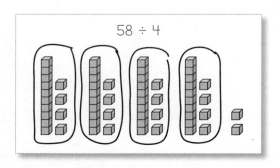

Math and Literature

WorldScapes Readers™

All Tied Up For activity suggestions for pp. 8–9 of *All Tied Up*, see *Guided Problem Solving for the Math Library.*

Math Project

 Social Studies

Factoid

The Christmas Bird Count is an annual tradition of the Audubon Society that started in 1900. Participants take a census of all the birds they see at a particular site on one day. During the 2005–2006 season, 57,156 observers reported seeing 61,579,355 birds.

Directions

Have students conduct their own survey of their favorite local animal. Have them spend 20 minutes outside each day for one week and count the number of times they spot their animal. At the end of the week, have them find a total number of sightings. Have them divide by the number of days they observed. Students should ignore the remainder. Tell students this is a good way to estimate the number of sightings each day.

Have students "publish" a page about their animal and their findings in a class book. Have the page include a drawing of their animal, one fact about their animal, and the estimated number of sightings each day.

> Blue Jay
>
> A blue jay is about 10 inches in length.

> I saw about 4 blue jays each day.

Home-School Connection

Home-School Connection Master

Name _____

Home-School Connection Topic **10** (English)

Developing Fluency: Dividing by 1-Digit Divisors

Dear Family,

In this topic, your child will learn how to divide with one-digit divisors. Learning this skill will require his or her understanding in the areas of estimating quotients, remainders, connecting models and symbols, dividing with one-digit divisors, and using zeros in quotients. You can expect to see work that provides practice in dividing whole numbers with one-digit divisors and checking the answer with multiplication and addition. Your child should continue to practice basic facts in multiplication and division.

Here is an activity that you can do with your child to help him or her learn about dividing by 1-digit divisors.

Variations on a Theme

Materials: Pencil, index cards

Step 1: Write a × symbol, a ÷ symbol, and an = symbol on three index cards.

Step 2: Write a one-digit number on an index card. Write a two- or three-digit number on another index card. Write the product on a third card.

Step 3: Ask your child to arrange the cards to create a multiplication sentence.

Step 4: Then challenge your child to use the cards to make a division sentence.

Step 5: Repeat the activity with different sets of numbers.

Purpose

Provide families with a quick overview of the content that will be taught in Topic 10. Read the Dear Family letter to the students and have them sign it. Also available in Spanish.

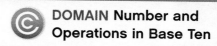

DOMAIN Number and Operations in Base Ten

Topic
10

Developing Fluency: Dividing by 1-Digit Divisors

▼ Selenium is an element found in certain materials, such as these selenite crystals. It is often used to conduct electricity. Some of the tallest selenite crystals are found in Chihuahua, Mexico. Find out how many times taller they are than a 4-foot-tall fourth grader in Lesson 10-4.

Topic Essential Questions
- How can repeated subtraction be used to model division?
- What is the standard procedure for dividing multi-digit numbers?

Review What You Know!

Vocabulary

Choose the best term from the box.

- array
- factors
- compatible numbers
- partial product

1. An arrangement of objects in rows and columns is called a(n) ? .
   Array
2. When multiplying a two-digit number by a two-digit number, a ? is found by multiplying the first factor by the ones of the second factor.
   Partial product
3. Numbers that are easy to compute mentally are called ? .
   Compatible numbers

Division Facts

Divide.

4. $15 \div 3$ **5.** $64 \div 8$ **6.** $72 \div 8$
  5   8   9
7. $35 \div 7$ **8.** $12 \div 4$ **9.** $45 \div 9$
  5   3   5

Multiplying by 10 and 100

Find each product.

10. 62×10 **11.** 24×100 **12.** 65×100
  620   2,400   6,500
13. 14×10 **14.** 35×100 **15.** 59×10
  140   3,500   590

Arrays

16. Write a multiplication problem for the array at the right.
    3×4

17. **Writing to Explain** Is an array for 4×3 the same or different from the array shown above? Explain.   **Different because the array for 4 × 3 would have 4 rows with 3 objects in each row.**

Topic 10   **225**

Review What You Know!

Purpose

Assign each set of exercises and go over the answers with students.

For full teacher support of each Problem-Based Interactive Learning activity, see the **Develop the Concept: Interactive** page of each lesson in the Topic 10 Teacher's Edition.

Lesson 10-1 Using Objects to Divide: Division as Repeated Subtraction

Purpose To understand that division with multi-digit dividends can be solved by repeatedly subtracting the divisor from the dividend as many times as possible

Ⓒ **Mathematical Practices**
- Use Appropriate Tools
- Model with Mathematics
- Communicate

Lesson 10-2 Division as Repeated Subtraction

Purpose To understand that division is a shortcut for repeatedly subtracting the same number

Ⓒ **Mathematical Practices**
- Reason Abstractly
- Use Appropriate Tools
- Model with Mathematics

Lesson 10-3 Using Objects to Divide: Division as Sharing

Purpose To understand that division with multi-digit dividends can be done by partitioning the total into equal groups

Ⓒ **Mathematical Practices**
- Use Appropriate Tools
- Model with Mathematics
- Communicate

Lesson 10-4 Dividing 2-Digit by 1-Digit Numbers

Purpose To understand that the steps in the division algorithm make sense when connected to the sharing (partitioning) interpretation for division

Ⓒ **Mathematical Practices**
- Make Generalizations
- Use Appropriate Tools
- Model with Mathematics

Topic
10

Interactive Learning Hands-On Minds-On

Pose the problem. Start each lesson by working together to solve problems. It will help you make sense of math.

Applying Math Practices
- What am I asked to find?
- What else can I try?
- How are quantities related?
- How can I explain my work?
- How can I use math to model the problem?
- Can I use tools to help?
- Is my work precise?
- Why does this work?
- How can I generalize?

Lesson 10-1

Ⓒ **Use Tools** Solve. Use counters if you want.

How many of the cans shown at the right are needed to hold 45 tennis balls? Show how you found the answer.

Lesson 10-2

Ⓒ **Reason** Solve this problem using only paper and pencil.

A certain bird feeder holds 6 cups of bird feed. How many times can this feeder be filled using a 72-cup bag of bird feed?

Lesson 10-3

Ⓒ **Use Tools** Solve. Use place-value blocks if you want.

Paulo has 39 patches from states he visited. He wants to arrange them on a board in 3 equal rows. How many patches will be in each row?

Lesson 10-4

Ⓒ **Generalize** Solve any way you choose.

Swati is packing T-shirts and shorts into boxes to put away for the winter. There are 42 items to pack. She packs the same number of items into 3 boxes. How many items does Swati pack in each box? Show how you found the answer.

MATHEMATICAL PRACTICES

MATHEMATICAL PRACTICES

Lesson 10-5

Generalize Solve. Use what you learned in the previous lesson to help.

All 5 grades at the school shown at the right have the same number of students. How many students are in each grade? Show how you found the answer.

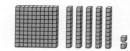
550 students

Lesson 10-6

Use Tools Show 152 using place value blocks. Share the blocks to solve this problem.

Roberto is using craft sticks to make picture frames. He has 152 craft sticks. He uses 6 sticks for each frame. How many frames can he make? Tell what you did with the blocks to solve the problem.

Lesson 10-7

Reasonableness Find two estimates for this problem. Tell how you found each.

A certain high school football stadium has 6 same-size sections. The stadium holds a total of 1,950 people. About how many people can be seated in each section? (a) Use estimation to give two multiples of 100 between which the exact quotient falls. (b) Then give a single number as an estimate of the quotient.

Lesson 10-8

Model Solve any way you choose. Show your work.

Susan has $45. She spends $15 on a book for her father, $20 on candles for her mother, and $6 on a board game for her brother. Does Susan have enough money left to buy a box of markers for $5?

$45			
15	20	6	x

Lesson 10-5 **Dividing 3-Digit by 1-Digit Numbers**

Purpose To understand that the steps in the division algorithm make sense when connected to the sharing (partitioning) interpretation for division and that the process is the same regardless of the size of the dividend

Mathematical Practices
- Make Generalizations
- Use Appropriate Tools
- Model with Mathematics

Lesson 10-6 **Deciding Where to Start Dividing**

Purpose To understand that place value and estimation can be used to determine the place value of the leading digit in a quotient

Mathematical Practices
- Use Appropriate Tools
- Make Generalizations
- Reason Abstractly

Lesson 10-7 **Dividing 4-Digit by 1-Digit Numbers**

Purpose To understand how estimation can be used to determine a reasonable quotient prior to finding the exact answer

Mathematical Practices
- Check for Reasonableness
- Reason Abstractly

Lesson 10-8 **Problem Solving: Multiple-Step Problems**

Purpose To understand that answers to hidden questions need to be found before finding the final answer to a multiple-step problem

Mathematical Practices
- Model with Mathematics
- Reason Quantitatively

Using Objects to Divide: Division as Repeated Subtraction

Domain

Number and Operations in Base Ten

Cluster

Use place value understanding and properties of operations to perform multi-digit arithmetic.

Standard

4.NBT.6 Find whole-number quotients and remainders with up to four-digit dividends and one-digit divisors, using strategies based on place value, the properties of operations, and/or the relationship between multiplication and division. Illustrate and explain the calculation by using equations, rectangular arrays, and/ or area models.

Mathematical Practices

○ Make sense of problems and persevere in solving them.

○ Reason abstractly and quantitatively.

✔ Construct viable arguments and critique the reasoning of others.

○ Model with mathematics.

✔ Use appropriate tools strategically.

○ Attend to precision.

○ Look for and make use of structure.

○ Look for and express regularity in repeated reasoning.

Lesson Overview

Objective	Essential Understanding	Vocabulary	Materials
Students will use repeated subtraction to model division.	Repeated subtraction situations can be modeled and solved using division.		Two-color counters (Teaching Tool 12)

PROFESSIONAL DEVELOPMENT

Math Background

Two interpretations for division are sharing and repeated subtraction. The steps in the standard algorithm for dividing whole numbers can best be explained using the sharing interpretation. However, another division algorithm for whole numbers exists based on the repeated subtraction interpretation.

This lesson and the next lesson develop this alternative algorithm. For 24 ÷ 2, the quotient is the number of times 2 can be subtracted from 24. Estimating how many 2s are in 24 and then subtracting a multiple of 2 from 24 can shorten this process. This lesson shows both approaches by connecting counters to the symbols.

1 Daily Common Core Review

Daily Common Core Review

Name _____

Daily Common Core Review
10-1

1. Melissa has 19 more stamps than George. If George has 24 stamps, how many stamps does Melissa have?

   A 33
   B 39
   Ⓒ 43
   D 45

2. **Mental Math** Madison's hair was 10 inches long before she got it cut. She had 3 inches cut off. How many inches long is her hair now?

   A 3 inches
   B 6 inches
   Ⓒ 7 inches
   D 13 inches

3. Which shows the numbers in order from greatest to least?

   A 24,500; 25,400; 24,900
   B 25,400; 24,500; 24,900
   Ⓒ 25,400; 24,900; 24,500
   D 24,500; 24,900; 25,400

4. Miguel is putting his books away on a bookcase. There are 5 shelves on the bookcase. Miguel has 30 books. How many books should Miguel put on each shelf so that each shelf has an equal number of books?

   6 books

5. Tamika had $15 to spend at the fair. She played a game for $2, rode on the Ferris wheel for $3, and bought a sandwich for $4. How much money did she have left? Show your work and explain how you found your answer.

   $6; Sample answer: $2 + $3 + $4 = $9, $15 − $9 = $6; I added to find the total amount spent and then subtracted that amount from $15 to find how much money was left.

Content Reviewed

Exercise 1   Addition

Exercise 2   Subtraction

Exercise 3   Comparing and Ordering Numbers

Exercise 4   Division

Exercise 5   Multiple-Step Problem

Also available in print

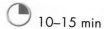

 10–15 min # Problem-Based Interactive Learning *Hands-On Minds-On*

Overview Students will use counters to solve division problems that involve repeated subtraction.

Focus How can repeated subtraction help you divide?

Materials Two-color counters (Teaching Tool 12)

 **Engage**

Set the Purpose *You have learned how to use mental math to solve division problems. Today we'll learn how to use repeated subtraction to solve division problems.*

Connect Point out that a collection of objects can be organized into equal groups. *How many piles of 5 objects can be made from a group of 10 total objects?* [2 piles]

MATHEMATICAL PRACTICES

Use Appropriate Tools
When students use counters to model division as repeated subtraction, they are using appropriate tools.

Pose the Problem *A can of tennis balls holds 3 balls. How many cans are needed to hold 45 tennis balls?* Have students work in pairs and share their solution strategies.

Use Prior Knowedge *You have learned that there are different interpretations for division. Today, we will use one of those to solve real-world division problems.*

Whole-Class Participation Have students share their solutions. *How many counters are needed for this problem?* [45] *How many go in each can?* [3] *If you place 3 in one can, how many balls remain?* [42] *How did you find this number?* [Subtract 45 − 3] *If you fill another can with 3 balls, how many remain?* [39] *How can this be continued to find the number of cans needed?* [Use repeated subtraction of 3 from the total until there are less than 3 tennis balls remaining.]

Model/Demonstrate Show one way of recording the work described above by repeatedly subtracting 3. This can be done 15 times so 15 cans are needed. Now show another way. *Can 10 cans be filled?* [Yes] *How many balls are used?* [10 × 3 = 30] *How many remain?* [45 − 30 = 15]. *How many cans are needed for the 15 balls and how many are used?* [5 cans, 5 × 3 = 15] *How many cans were filled?* [10 + 5 = 15 cans]. Show how to record this as shown at the right. Then show how multiplication can be used to check the answer 15 × 3 = 45.

$$\begin{array}{r} 45 \\ -30 \\ \hline 15 \end{array}$$ 10 groups of 3, $10 \times \underline{3}$

$$\begin{array}{r} -15 \\ \hline 0 \end{array}$$ 5 groups of 3, $5 \times \underline{3}$

$10 + 5 = 15$ 15 cans are needed

 Extend

Find two ways to use repeated subtraction to solve this problem and record each way with paper and pencil. *A fully loaded truck holds 2 tons of gravel. How many truckloads are needed to move 26 tons of gravel?* [13 truckloads]

Visual Learning

Using Objects to Divide: Division as Repeated Subtraction

How can subtraction help you divide?

Su has 24 international postage stamps. She needs 2 of these stamps to send a postcard. How many postcards can she send using all of these stamps?

24 stamps

Think How many 2s are in 24?

Why is this a division situation? [Finding how many 2s are in 24 is the same as finding how many times 2 can be subtracted from 24; this can be modeled using division.]

---

1 **Visual Learning**

Set the Purpose Call students' attention to the **Visual Learning Bridge** at the top of the page. *In this lesson you will learn to use repeated subtraction to divide.*

2 **Guided Practice** | **MATHEMATICAL PRACTICES**

Tell students that they may use counters and repeated subtraction to model the division in each exercise.

Exercise 3
Error Intervention

If students are having difficulty explaining the shortcut,

then ask: *How many groups of 2 are in 10?* [5] *How many groups of 2 are in 4?* [2]

Reteaching Use counters to show how repeated subtraction is used to divide. Have students model 30 ÷ 3 with counters. For another example and more practice, assign **Reteaching** Set A on p. 248.

3 **Independent Practice**

For Exercises 4–17, remind students to use counters to model the division as repeated subtraction.

Lesson
10-1

Common Core

4.NBT.6 Find whole-number quotients and remainders with up to four-digit dividends and one-digit divisors, using strategies based on place value, the properties of operations, and/or the relationship between multiplication and division. Illustrate and explain the calculation by using equations, rectangular arrays, and/or area models.

Using Objects to Divide: Division as Repeated Subtraction

How can subtraction help you divide?

Su has 24 international postage stamps. She needs 2 of these stamps to send a postcard. How many postcards can she send using all of these stamps?

24 stamps

Think How many 2s are in 24?

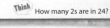

Guided Practice* | **MATHEMATICAL PRACTICES**

Do you know HOW?

Use counters and repeated subtraction to divide. Record your work.

1. How many 3s are in 48?
   16
2. How many 4s are in 60?
   15

Do you UNDERSTAND?

 3. **Writing to Explain** Explain the shortcut this student used for solving the postcard problem above.

24 − 10 = 14 (5 groups of 2)
14 − 10 = 4 (5 more groups of 2)
  4 − 4 = 0 (2 more groups of 2)

12 postcards **See margin.**

Independent Practice

For **4** through **17** use counters and repeated subtraction to divide. Record your work.

4. How many 5s are in 35?
   7
5. How many 4s are in 32?
   8
6. How many 7s are in 84?
   12
7. How many 6s are in 66?
   11
8. How many 8s are in 72?
   9
9. How many 3s are in 57?
   19

10. 56 ÷ 7
    8
11. 54 ÷ 9
    6
12. 30 ÷ 2
    15
13. 84 ÷ 6
    14
14. 80 ÷ 5
    16
15. 112 ÷ 8
    14
16. 88 ÷ 8
    11
17. 117 ÷ 9
    13

228 *For another example, see Set A on page 248.*

3. 10 as 5 groups of 2 was subtracted from 24 to get 14 (24 − 10 = 14). 10 as 5 more groups of 2 was subtracted from 14 to get 4 (14 − 10 = 4). 4 as 2 groups of 2 was subtracted to get 0 (4 − 4 = 0). 5 + 5 + 2 = 12.

ELL
STRATEGY
Visual
Learning

Visual Learning Animation
www.pearsonsuccessnet.com or CD

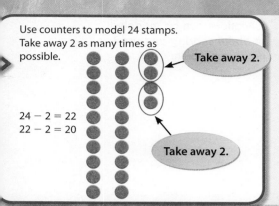

Use counters to model 24 stamps. Take away 2 as many times as possible.

Take away 2.

Take away 2.

24 − 2 = 22
22 − 2 = 20

Does it matter which two stamps are taken away each time? [No]

Continue to take away 2 as many times as possible. Record using symbols.

20 − 2 = 18	10 − 2 = 8
18 − 2 = 16	8 − 2 = 6
16 − 2 = 14	6 − 2 = 4
14 − 2 = 12	4 − 2 = 2
12 − 2 = 10	2 − 2 = 0

Since 2 was subtracted 12 times, Su can send 12 postcards.

What multiplication equation can be used to check this answer? [2 × 12 = 24]

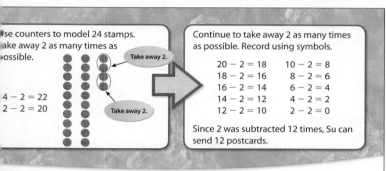

Use counters to model 24 stamps. Take away 2 as many times as possible.

Take away 2.

Take away 2.

4 − 2 = 22
2 − 2 = 20

Continue to take away 2 as many times as possible. Record using symbols.

20 − 2 = 18	10 − 2 = 8
18 − 2 = 16	8 − 2 = 6
16 − 2 = 14	6 − 2 = 4
14 − 2 = 12	4 − 2 = 2
12 − 2 = 10	2 − 2 = 0

Since 2 was subtracted 12 times, Su can send 12 postcards.

Problem Solving © **MATHEMATICAL PRACTICES**

Students use counters and repeated subtraction for Exercises 18–24. Remind students to check for reasonableness when solving each problem.

Exercise 22

© **Critique the Reasoning of Others** Remind students that they first need to determine the dividend (the total number of marbles) and the divisor (the number of groups). Also remind students to explain why Paul is correct or incorrect.

Early Finishers Have each student write a problem like those on this page and have a fellow student solve the problem.

Problem Solving © **MATHEMATICAL PRACTICES**

18. Teams of 4 students will be formed for a scavenger hunt. How many teams will be formed if 52 students signed up?
13 teams

20. Billy is organizing his football cards into 3 equal stacks. How many cards should he put in each stack if he has a total of 75 football cards?

A 15   **C 25**
B 20   D 40

22. Critique Reasoning Paul claims that when he organizes his collection of 70 marbles into 5 equal piles that there will be 15 marbles in each pile. Is Paul correct? Why or why not?
See margin.

23. The 240 students at Cypress Elementary are taking a field trip. How many vans are needed to transport the students, if each van will hold 8 students? **30 vans**

19. Mary wants to share her collection of 42 marbles equally among 3 of her friends. How many marbles will each of her friends receive?
14 marbles

21. A pizza is cut into 12 pieces for 4 people to share equally. How many pieces will each person receive?

(A) 3   C 1
B 2   D 0

70 marbles in all

24. Jeff buys a box of 30 apples. He eats 2 apples each day at lunch. How long will the apples last?
15 days

22. Paul is incorrect; 15 × 5 = 75, but Paul only has 70 marbles. Since 75 − 70 = 5, there will be 1 less marble in each group or 14 marbles in each group.

229

Close

Essential Understanding Repeated subtraction situations can be modeled and solved using division. *In this lesson, you thought about sharing and used repeated subtraction to help understand and solve division problems.*

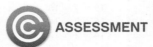 **ASSESSMENT**

Exercises 1 and 2 are worth 1 point each.
Use the rubric to score Exercise 3.

Exercise 3

Writing to Explain Students should find the number of piles of stickers and explain how to use repeated subtraction to arrive at the answer.

ELL **Suggest a Sequence** For students who need additional writing support, provide this sequence to help them structure their answers: *First, find the _____ [number] you want to divide. Next, find the number of _____ [objects] in each group. Lastly, solve the problem by finding how many times you can subtract the number of objects in each group from the total number of objects.*

Student Samples
3-point answer The student writes an equation that fits the situation given and provides a clear explanation.

> $40 \div 8 = 5$. There are 40 stickers and 8 stickers in each pile. I subtracted 8 from 40 five times and there were no more stickers. So, there are 5 piles of 8 stickers each with no extra stickers.

2-point answer The student shows understanding of division but does not provide a thorough explanation.

> $40 \div 8 = 5$. The stickers should be placed into 5 groups.

1-point answer The student does not offer any explanation or shows no understanding of division as repeated subtraction.

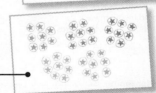

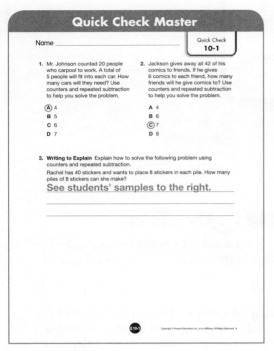

 **Formative Assessment**

Use the **Quick Check** to assess students' understanding.

Prescription for Differentiated Instruction
Use student work on the **Quick Check** to prescribe differentiated instruction.

Points	Prescription
0–2	Intervention
3–4	On-Level
5	Advanced

Differentiated Instruction

Intervention

Using Objects to Divide: Division as Repeated Subtraction

 10–15 min

Materials Two-color counters (or Teaching Tool 12)

- Divide students into pairs. Give each pair 30 counters.

- Ask students to model 24 ÷ 3 by using 24 counters and separating them into 3 equal groups. Have students move counters into the 3 groups, one at a time, until all 24 counters are used. Then have them count the number in each group. Ask them what 24 divided into 3 equal groups is.

- Repeat for 27 divided into 9 equal groups and 30 divided into 5 equal groups.

On-Level

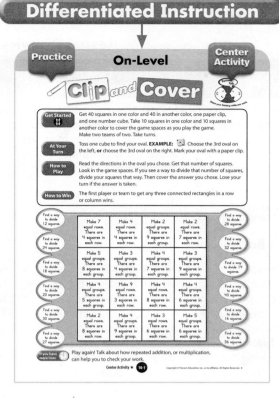

Practice / **Center Activity**

Advanced

Practice / **Center Activity**

ELL Report Back To check understanding, ask a student to repeat and complete this sentence: *If I start with 30 counters and I put 6 counters in each group, the number of groups I can make is _____.* [5]

Leveled Homework

Reteaching Master

Name _____
Reteaching 10-1

Using Objects to Divide: Division as Repeated Subtraction

When you divide, you subtract equal groups.

Doris has 32 strawberries. She makes box lunches by putting 4 strawberries in each box lunch. How many box lunches can she make this way?

What you think: Doris will put 4 strawberries in each lunch box. How many lunch boxes can she make?

What you show: Repeated subtraction

32 − 4 = 28   16 − 4 = 12
28 − 4 = 24   12 − 4 = 8
24 − 4 = 20   8 − 4 = 4
20 − 4 = 16   4 − 4 = 0

You can subtract 4 from 32 eight times.

What you write: 32 ÷ 4 = 8

32 is the dividend, the number that is being divided.

4 is the divisor, the number the dividend is being divided by.

8 is the quotient, or the answer to the division problem.

Draw pictures to solve each problem.

1. You have 15 marbles. You put 5 marbles into each group. How many groups can you make?
   3 groups

2. You have 20 ice cubes. You put 4 ice cubes into each glass. How many glasses can you put ice cubes into?
   5 glasses

Also available in print

Practice Master

Name _____
Practice 10-1

Using Objects to Divide: Division as Repeated Subtraction

Draw pictures to solve each problem.

1. Anthony has 18 stickers. He wants to give 3 stickers to each of his friends. How many friends can he give stickers to?
   6 friends; Students' drawings may vary.

2. Mrs. Riggins has 40 glass tiles. She is going to put 8 glass tiles on each clay pot she is decorating. How many clay pots can she decorate this way?
   5 clay pots; Students' drawings may vary.

3. There are 21 students in Mr. Tentler's class. The class is being separated into groups of 3 students. How many groups can they form?
   7 groups; Students' drawings may vary.

4. Calvin reads a book that has 90 pages. If he reads 10 pages each day, how many days will it take him to finish reading the book?
   A 3 days
   B 6 days
   C 9 days
   D 12 days

5. A school district has 24 flags to give to schools. If it gives 4 flags to each school, how many schools can it give flags to? Explain your answer.
   6 schools; Sample answer: I subtracted 4 from 24 six times and there were no flags left over.

Also available in print

Enrichment Master

Name _____
Enrichment 10-1

Just the Fact(or)s

Some numbers have several factors. Complete the following to find all of the factors of 12. The first one is done for you.

1. = 12 in a group
   12
   1 group

2. = 6 in a group
   12
   2 groups

3. = **3** in a group
   12
   4 groups

4. = **__ in a group**
   12
   3 groups

5. There are 6 numbers that are factors of 12. What are they?
   12, 6, 4, 3, 2, 1

Also available in print

 DIGITAL Game **Math Facts Practice** www.pearsonsuccessnet.com

 DIGITAL eTools **Counters** www.pearsonsuccessnet.com

 DIGITAL eTools **Place-Value Blocks** www.pearsonsuccessnet.com

Division as Repeated Subtraction

 **Lesson Overview**

Objective	Essential Understanding	Vocabulary	Materials
Students will record division as repeated subtraction.	Repeated subtraction situations can be solved using a division algorithm different from the standard algorithm.		

Domain

Number and Operations in Base Ten

Cluster

Use place value understanding and properties of operations to perform multi-digit arithmetic.

Standard

4.NBT.6 Find whole-number quotients and remainders with up to four-digit dividends and one-digit divisors, using strategies based on place value, the properties of operations, and/or the relationship between multiplication and division. Illustrate and explain the calculation by using equations, rectangular arrays, and/or area models.

Mathematical Practices

○ Make sense of problems and persevere in solving them.

✔ Reason abstractly and quantitatively.

✔ Construct viable arguments and critique the reasoning of others.

○ Model with mathematics.

○ Use appropriate tools strategically.

○ Attend to precision.

○ Look for and make use of structure.

○ Look for and express regularity in repeated reasoning.

 PROFESSIONAL DEVELOPMENT

Math Background

This lesson continues work with the alternative algorithm for dividing whole numbers based on the repeated subtraction interpretation. A key idea to make explicit here is that there are multiple ways to find the quotient for a problem like 24 ÷ 2. One might begin by thinking that there are at least 5 twos in 24, subtracting 10 from 24, and then repeating the process. Or one might begin by thinking that there are at least 10 twos in 24, subtracting 20, and then continuing. Estimation helps identify a multiple of the divisor close to the dividend. Using multiples of 10 as benchmarks makes the estimation process easier.

1 Daily Common Core Review

Daily Common Core Review

Name _____

Daily Common Core Review **10-2**

1. **Mental Math** Alexandra has 24 flowers. She puts the same number of flowers in each of her vases. How many flowers will be in each vase?

A 3
B 4
Ⓒ 8
D 12

2. Diana drew a shape which was divided into equal parts. Which shape did Diana draw?

A ○
B △
Ⓒ ⊞
D ⬡

3. Which shows the numbers in order from least to greatest?

A 9,856; 9,865; 9,964; 9,846
B 9,856; 9,846; 9,865; 9,964
C 9,964; 9,846; 9,865; 9,856
Ⓓ 9,846; 9,856; 9,864; 9,965

4. Henry wants to buy a pair of speakers that cost $325. So far, he has saved $157. How much more does Henry have to save to buy the speakers?

$168

5. Heather wrote a basic multiplication fact, but she covered up some of the numbers. What multiplication fact did she write? Explain how you found the missing numbers.

☐ × ☐ = 49

7 × 7 = 49; Sample answer: I thought of multiplication facts and 7 × 7 has a product of 49.

Also available in print

Content Reviewed

Exercise 1   Division

Exercise 2   Equal Parts of Regions

Exercise 3   Comparing and Ordering Whole Numbers

Exercise 4   Subtraction

Exercise 5   Multiplication Facts

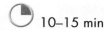 10–15 min # Problem-Based Interactive Learning

Overview Students will use an algorithm for dividing that is based on repeated subtraction.

Focus How can recording division as repeated subtraction help you divide?

Set the Purpose *You have learned how to use repeated subtraction to solve division problems. Today we'll learn how to record division using a repeated subtraction algorithm.*

Connect Point out that a collection of objects can be organized into equal groups. *How many piles of 4 objects can be made from a group of 64 total objects?* [16 piles]

 MATHEMATICAL PRACTICES

Reason Quantitatively
When students use a repeated subtraction algorithm to record division, they reason quantitatively.

Pose the Problem *Solve this problem without using counters or pictures. Instead, show how to divide using paper and pencil. A certain bird feeder holds 6 cups of bird feed. How many times can this feeder be filled using a 72-cup bag of bird seed?*

Use Prior Knowledge *In the previous lesson you used counters to solve repeated subtraction division problems and you recorded your work with paper and pencil. Today you will solve the same type of problems but you will use the recording methods but no counters.*

Model/Demonstrate Have students share their solutions. Be sure to show at least two ways of recording the work with paper and pencil. As you ask these questions, show how to record the work. *Why is this a repeated subtraction division situation?* [You are asked to find how many 6s are in 72.] *Do you think that there are more than ten 6s in 72 or fewer than ten 6s in 72?* [10 × 6 = 60; so there are more than 10] *If you take ten 6s away from 72, how much remains?* [72 − 60 = 12]. *How can this be recorded?* [See student work at the right] *How many 6s are in 12?* [two; 2 × 6 = 12]. *How can this be recorded?* [See student work at the right] *So, how many 6s all together are in 72?* [10 + 2 = 12] *How can you decide if this answer is reasonable?* [Use multiplication; 12 × 6 = 72] *Show another way to do the same calculation.* [See student work at the right]

$$
\begin{array}{r}
72 \\
\underline{-60} \\
12 \\
\underline{-12} \\
0
\end{array}
$$
Take away ten 6s, 10 × 6 = 60

Take two more 6s away, 2 × 6 = 12

10 + 2 = 12 There were twelve 6s taken away.

$$
\begin{array}{r}
72 \\
\underline{-36} \\
36 \\
\underline{-36} \\
0
\end{array}
$$
Take away six 6s, 6 × 6 = 36

Take six more 6s away, 6 × 6 = 36

6 + 6 = 12 There were twelve 6s taken away.

Use the same process as above and show two ways to find how many groups of 5 objects can be made from a collection of 70 objects. [14 groups]

3 Develop the Concept: Visual

Visual Learning

Division as Repeated Subtraction

How can you record division using repeated subtraction?

Each row on an airplane can seat 3 people. If there are 63 people waiting in line and each seat will be taken, how many rows of seats are needed?

Think How many 3s are in 63?

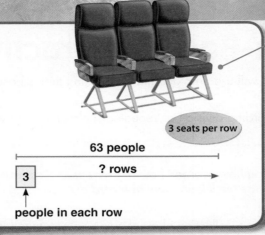

3 seats per row

63 people

3 | ? rows →

people in each row

Why is this a division situation?
[Finding how many 3s are in 63 is the same as finding how many times 3 can be subtracted from 63; this can be modeled using division.]

---

1 Visual Learning

Set the Purpose Call students' attention to the **Visual Learning Bridge** at the top of the page. *In this lesson you will learn how to record division as repeated subtraction without using models or counters.*

2 Guided Practice — MATHEMATICAL PRACTICES

Tell students that they can start with a multiple of the divisor that is less than the dividend.

Exercise 5
Error Intervention

If students are having difficulty determining a multiple of the divisor to start with,

then ask: *How many groups of 3 are in 30?* [10] *How many groups of 3 are in 60?* [20] *How many groups of 3 are in 9?* [3]

Reteaching Use the repeated subtraction algorithm to record 60 ÷ 4 using paper and pencil. For another example and more practice, assign **Reteaching** Set B on p. 248.

3 Independent Practice

For Exercises 7 through 14, remind students to use the repeated subtraction algorithm to record their work.

Problem Solving — MATHEMATICAL PRACTICES

For Exercises 15 and 16, remind students to draw the bar diagram provided along with a multiple of the divisor that is less than the dividend when beginning the exercises. Also remind the students to record their work using the repeated subtraction algorithm.

Lesson 10-2

Common Core
4.NBT.6 Find whole-number quotients and remainders with up to four-digit dividends and one-digit divisors, using strategies based on place value, the properties of operations, and/or the relationship between multiplication and division. Illustrate and explain the calculation by using equations, rectangular arrays, and/or area models.

Division as Repeated Subtraction

How can you record division using repeated subtraction?

Each row on an airplane can seat 3 people. If there are 63 people waiting in line and each seat will be taken, how many rows of seats are needed?

Think How many 3s are in 63?

3 seats per row

63 people

3 | ? rows

people in each row

Guided Practice* — MATHEMATICAL PRACTICES

Do you know HOW?

Use repeated subtraction to divide. Record your work.

1. 48 ÷ 4
   See margin.
2. 75 ÷ 5
   See margin.
3. 153 ÷ 9
   See margin.
4. 65 ÷ 5
   See margin.

Do you UNDERSTAND?

Use repeated subtraction to divide. Record your work.

5. **Reason** Show one way of using repeated subtraction to solve. 69 ÷ 3. See margin.

6. **Reason** Show another way of using repeated subtraction to solve 69 ÷ 3. See margin.

Independent Practice

For **7** through **14** use repeated subtraction to divide. Record your work. Student work will vary.

7. 78 ÷ 6   8. 84 ÷ 7   9. 88 ÷ 8   10. 42 ÷ 3
   13   12   11   14

11. 90 ÷ 6   12. 40 ÷ 2   13. 92 ÷ 4   14. 126 ÷ 7
    15   20   23   18

Problem Solving — MATHEMATICAL PRACTICES

15. There are 5 players on a basketball team. How many teams can be formed from a list of 90 players?

     90 players
    5 | ? teams →
    players on each team   **18 teams**

16. A collection of 64 stickers is being placed into 4 equal piles. How many stickers will be placed in each pile?

    64 stickers
    ? | ? | ? | ?
    stickers in each pile   **16 sticker**

*For another example, see Set B on page 248.

---

1. 12; Sample answer: 48 − 40 = 8, 8 − 8 = 0
2. 15; Sample answer: 75 − 50 = 25, 25 − 25 = 0
3. 17; Sample answer: 153 − 90 = 63, 63 − 63 = 0
4. 13; Sample answer: 65 − 50 = 15, 15 − 15 = 0
5. 23; Sample answer: 69 − 30 = 30, 39 − 30 = 9, 9 − 9 = 0
6. 23; Sample answer: 69 − 60 = 9, 9 − 9 = 0

Here is one way to record the division problem
63 ÷ 3.

  63   Estimate: How many 3s are in 63? Try 10.
−30 Multiply 10 × 3 and subtract.
  33   Estimate: How many 3s are in 33? Use 11.
−33 Multiply 11 × 3 and subtract.
   0

    10 + 11 = 21, so there are 21 3s in 63.

21 rows are needed to seat 63 people.

Why did you subtract 10 3s from 63 first?
[It was easier to multiply 10 × 3 = 30, than it would be to multiply some other number by 3.]

Here is another way to record the
division problem.

  63   Estimate: How many 3s are in 63? Try 20.
−60 Multiply 20 × 3 and subtract.
   3   Estimate: How many 3s are in 3? Use 1.
−3 Multiply 1 × 3 and subtract.
  0

    20 + 1 = 21, so there are 21 3s in 63.

21 rows are needed to seat 63 people.

What multiplication equation can be used to check this answer?
[21 × 3 = 63]

---

ere is one way to record the division
roblem 63 ÷ 3.

 63 Estimate: How many 3s are in 63? Try 10.
30 Multiply 10 × 3 and subtract.
33 Estimate: How many 3s are in 33? Use 11.
33 Multiply 11 × 3 and subtract.
 0

  10 + 11 = 21, so there are 21
  3s in 63.

1 rows are needed to seat 63 people.

Here is another way to record the
division problem.

  63 Estimate: How many 3s are in 63? Try 20.
−60 Multiply 20 × 3 and subtract.
   3 Estimate: How many 3s are in 3? Use 1.
−3 Multiply 1 × 3 and subtract.
  0

   20 + 1 = 21, so there are 21
  3s in 63.

21 rows are needed to seat 63 people.

7. Which statement below is the best estimate for the quotient 99 ÷ 3?

A between 0 and 10

B between 10 and 20

C between 20 and 30

D between 30 and 40

18. There are 2 dozen eggs in the kitchen. A chef is baking cookies for 3 birthday parties. For each party, the chef is using an equal number of eggs. How many eggs does the chef use for one party? **8 eggs**

 12 eggs = 1 dozen

9. **Critique Reasoning** Amanda thinks that she can separate her books into 7 equal piles. Amanda has a total of 42 books. Is Amanda's reasoning correct? **See margin.**

42 books

20. A photo album can hold 84 pictures. If 4 pictures are on each page, then how many pages are in the photo album?

A 25   C 20

B 21   D 16

1. **Construct Arguments** Ryan has a total of 85 pennies. Will he be able to give away his pennies equally to 4 of his friends? Explain your reasoning. **See margin.**

22. A local baker made 132 bagels one day. The baker sells bagels in packages of 6 bagels. He sold all of the bagels. How many packages of bagels did he sell? **22 packages**

3. **Communicate** How can you use repeated subtraction to divide 81 ÷ 3? Solve and explain your process.
÷ 3 = 27; Sample answer: I subtracted 0, or 10 × 3, twice. Then I subtracted ven more 3s to get to 0. So I subtracted total of 10 + 10 + 7 = 27 3s.

24. A shoe store got a delivery of 104 pairs of shoes. There are 8 pairs of shoes in each case that was delivered. How many cases were delivered? **13 cases**

Lesson 10-2 **231**

Exercise 17
Ask the students the following questions. *How many groups of 3 objects can be formed from 9 objects?* [3 groups] *How many groups of 3 objects can be formed from 90 objects?* [30 groups]

Exercise 18
Remind the students that there are 12 eggs in a dozen.

Exercise 21
© **Construct Arguments** Remind students that they first need to determine the dividend (or the total number of pennies) as well as the divisor (or the number of friends). Also remind the students to use the repeated subtraction algorithm when recording their work and to explain whether or not Ryan will be able to share all of his pennies equally.

---

19. Amanda is correct; 42 ÷ 7 = 6, each pile will have 6 books and all of the books will be placed in a pile.

21. No; 85 ÷ 4 = 21 R1, each friend will receive 21 pennies, but Ryan will have 1 penny left.

4 Close/Assess and Differentiate

Close

Essential Understanding Repeated subtraction situations can be solved using a division algorithm different from the standard algorithm. *In this lesson, you learned how to record division as repeated subtraction.*

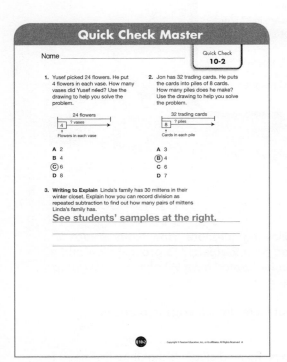

Formative Assessment

Use the **Quick Check** to assess students' understanding.

© ASSESSMENT

Exercises 1 and 2 are worth 1 point each. Use the rubric to score Exercise 3.

Exercise 3

Writing to Explain Students explain how to record division as repeated subtraction to find the number of groups of 2 in 30.

ELL Rephrase For students who need extra language support, read the word problem together. Encourage students to rephrase the problem or say it in their own words. Assist with the meaning of *pairs*, as needed.

Student Samples
3-point answer The student clearly and completely explains how to record division as repeated subtraction to find the number of equal groups in a total number of objects.

2-point answer The student does not provide a thorough explanation.

1-point answer The student does not show understanding of recording division as repeated subtraction.

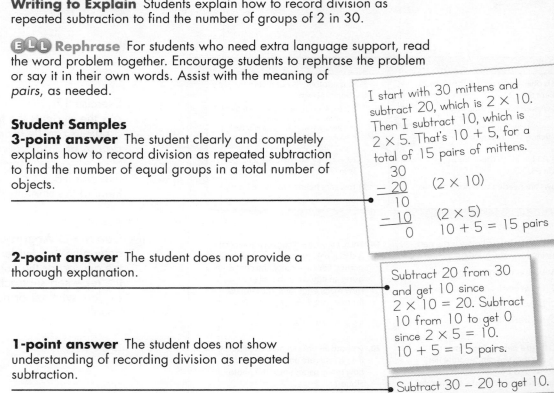

Prescription for Differentiated Instruction
Use student work on the **Quick Check** to prescribe differentiated instruction.

Points	Prescription
0–2	Intervention
3–4	On-Level
5	Advanced

Differentiated Instruction

Intervention

Recording Division as Repeated Subtraction

 10–15 min

- Ask students to record division as repeated subtraction to find how many 3s are in 33. Have them subtract $33 - 30$ to get 3, since $3 \times 10 = 30$. Then have them subtract 3 from 3 to get 0, since $3 \times 1 = 3$. Ask them how many 3s are in 24.

- Repeat for the number of 4s in 28 and the number of 5s in 30.

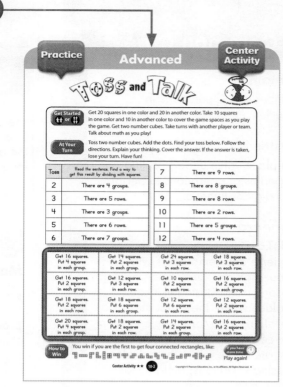

ELL **Partner Talk** Listen for evidence that a student is counting only complete and equal groups to find out how many groups there are in all. For example, a student might say, "Now every group has 5 squares, so I am ready to count all of the groups."

Leveled Homework

Reteaching Master

Division as Repeated Subtraction

Reteaching 10-2

For City Clean-Up Day, 18 people volunteered to clean up the city park. The volunteers worked in groups with 3 people each. How many groups of volunteers cleaned up the city park?

Use repeated subtraction to find the number of groups.

$18 - 3 = 15$
$15 - 3 = 12$
$12 - 3 = 9$
$9 - 3 = 6$
$6 - 3 = 3$
$3 - 3 = 0$

You subtract 3 six times.

There are 6 groups of volunteers.

Use repeated subtraction to divide. Use a number line to help.

1. Mark is placing 12 model cars into equal groups. Each group has 4 model cars. How many groups of model cars will he make?
3 groups

2. There are 24 students in gym class. They divided into teams of 6 for a volleyball game. How many teams were there?
4 teams

3. Each necklace Cara makes has 5 beads. How many necklaces can Cara make with 20 beads?
4 necklaces

4. Amy has 12 dolls in her collection. She places 6 dolls on each shelf. How many shelves does she need?
2 shelves

5. Charlie has 16 chores to do. He can complete 4 chores in one day. How many days will Charlie take to complete his chores?
4 days

6. The pet store has 9 parakeets. If 3 parakeets are in each cage, how many cages are there?
3 cages

7. Shawn needs to learn how to play 15 songs for his band's concert. If he learns 3 songs each week, how many weeks will it take him to learn all of the songs?
5 weeks

8. At Rosa Elementary School, 27 teachers signed up to carpool. If 3 teachers ride together in each car, how many cars are needed for all of the teachers?
9 cars

Also available in print

Practice Master

Division as Repeated Subtraction

Practice 10-2

Use repeated subtraction to solve each problem. Draw pictures to help.

1. Roger buys a package of 16 rawhide bones for his dog. He gives his dog 4 bones each week. How many weeks will the package of rawhide bones last?
Check students' drawings; 4 weeks

2. During recess 24 students divided into kickball teams. Each team had 6 players. How many teams were there?
Check students' drawings; 4 teams

3. Each member of a juggling troop juggles 6 balls at one time. The jugglers use 18 balls during a show. How many jugglers are in the show?
Check students' drawings; 3 jugglers

4. The county fair has 4 people working at the snack bar each shift. If 32 people work at the snack bar each day, how many shifts are there?
Check students' drawings; 8 shifts

5. For a piano recital, Jessie is playing a song that is 3 minutes long. She practices by playing the song several times in a row. If she practices for 21 minutes, how many times does she play the song?
A 6   **B** 7   C 8   D 9

6. Ryan wants to prepare for a mini-marathon by jogging 12 miles each week. How many days would he need to jog if he runs only 3 miles each day? Explain.
Sample answer: Ryan would have to run 4 days each week. There are 4 groups of three in 12.

Also available in print

Enrichment Master

Find the Missing Numbers

Enrichment 10-2

Use multiplication and division to complete each table.

1.

Number of Bicycles	1	6	2	9	5	8	3	7	4
Number of Wheels	2	12	4	18	10	16	6	14	8

2.

Number of ATVs	1	5	3	8	9	7	2	4	6
Number of Tires	3	15	9	24	27	21	6	12	18

3.

Number of Ants	1	7	4	5	2	9	6	3	8
Number of Legs	6	42	24	30	12	54	36	18	48

4.

Number of Spiders	1	9	6	2	4	8	3	7	5
Number of Legs	8	72	48	16	32	64	24	56	40

Also available in print

 Game **Math Facts Practice**
www.pearsonsuccessnet.com

DIGITAL eTools **Counters**
www.pearsonsuccessnet.com

DIGITAL eTools **Place-Value Blocks**
www.pearsonsuccessnet.com

Using Objects to Divide: Division as Sharing

Domain

Number and Operations in Base Ten

Cluster

Use place value understanding and properties of operations to perform multi-digit arithmetic.

Standard

4.NBT.6 Find whole-number quotients and remainders with up to four-digit dividends and one-digit divisors, using strategies based on place value, the properties of operations, and/or the relationship between multiplication and division. Illustrate and explain the calculation by using equations, rectangular arrays, and/or area models. Also **4.NBT.1**

Mathematical Practices

✔ Make sense of problems and persevere in solving them.

✔ Reason abstractly and quantitatively.

✔ Construct viable arguments and critique the reasoning of others.

○ Model with mathematics.

✔ Use appropriate tools strategically.

○ Attend to precision.

✔ Look for and make use of structure.

✔ Look for and express regularity in repeated reasoning.

 **Lesson Overview**

Objective	Essential Understanding	Vocabulary	Materials
Students will use place value to understand the algorithm of long division.	The sharing interpretataion of division can be used to model the standard division algorithm.		Place-value blocks (Teaching Tool 8) (4 tens rods and 13 unit cubes per pair), Blank recording sheet (per student)

Ⓒ **PROFESSIONAL DEVELOPMENT**

Math Background

Earlier in the year, students used partial products to find the answer to a multiplication problem. This lesson uses place value in a similar manner to divide.

The example at the top of pp. 232–233 shows the concept that division is breaking a whole into equal-sized groups.

Think of $57 \div 3$ as sorting 57 unit cubes into groups of 3.

Use $30 \div 3 = 10$.

This means 30 of the cubes can be sorted into 10 groups of 3.

If $30 - 3 = 27$ cubes are used, there are 27 cubes remaining.

Use $27 \div 3 = 9$.

This means the 27 remaining cubes can be sorted into 9 groups of 3.

There are no cubes remaining.

Add to find the total number of groups.

$10 + 9 = 19$

Therefore, $57 \div 3 = 19$.

1 Daily Common Core Review

Daily Common Core Review

Name _____

Daily Common Core Review
10-3

1. Wayne bought 6 football tickets. Each ticket cost $26. How much money did he spend?
   A $186
   B $182
   C $176
   Ⓓ $156

2. There are 35 boxes of soup cans on a delivery truck. How many cans of soup are on the delivery truck if there are 30 cans in each box?
   Ⓐ 1,050 cans
   B 850 cans
   C 625 cans
   D 425 cans

3. Andrea reads 36 pages each night. How many pages does she read in 42 nights?
   A 1,502
   Ⓑ 1,512
   C 1,552
   D 1,582

4. Daniel recycles 48 aluminum cans a week. How many cans does he recycle in 51 weeks?
   Ⓐ 2,448
   B 2,051
   C 584
   D 99

5. **Mental Math** Mugs cost $2 each. How much would it cost to buy 6 mugs?
   $12

6. Richard ran 12 laps around a 400-meter track. How many meters did Richard run in all?
   4,800 meters

7. Round 6,852 to the nearest thousand.
   7,000

Also available in print

Content Reviewed

Exercise 1   Multiplication

Exercise 2   Multiplication

Exercise 3   Multiplication

Exercise 4   Multiplication

Exercise 5   Multiplication

Exercise 6   Multiplication

Exercise 7   Rounding Whole Numbers

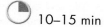

Problem-Based Interactive Learning

 Hands-On Minds-On

10–15 min

Overview Students will use place-value blocks to model dividing beyond basic facts.

Focus How can place value help you divide?

Materials Place-value blocks or Teaching Tool 8, 4 tens rods and 13 unit cubes (*per pair of students*)

Engage

Connect *Think of something that can be divided into 3 equal groups.* [Sample answers: An hour can be divided into three 20-minute time periods, a group of 60 people can be divided into 3 equal groups, a flag can have 3 equal parts.] *Sometimes there are situations in which you need to divide numbers beyond basic facts. Today, we will model how to do this.*

MATHEMATICAL PRACTICES

Use Appropriate Tools
When students use place-value blocks to model division, they are using appropriate tools.

Pose the Problem *Paulo has 39 patches from states that he and his relatives have visited. He wants to pin them onto a board. Paulo wants to arrange the patches on the board in 3 rows. How many patches will be in each row?* Have students work in pairs to solve the problem.

Link to Prior Knowledge *You worked with division in previous lessons. Based on what you've done before, what are some ways to model and solve this problem?* [You can draw a diagram. You can use or draw counters.] *Today, we will learn another way to solve this problem using place value.*

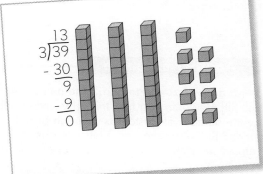

Whole-Class Discussion Have students share their solution strategies. Help students learn a way to record their work efficiently. Distribute place-value blocks to students. *How would we model 39 with place-value blocks?* [3 tens rods and 9 unit cubes] *Show how you could divide the blocks into 3 equal groups.* Allow students time to divide the blocks. *Let's examine what you just did. Put your blocks back together to show 39.* Write 3)39 on the board. *First show me how you divided the tens. How many tens are in each group?* [1] *We can write each action we take with the blocks on the board. Since there was one ten in each of the 3 groups, we will write 1 above the tens place in the quotient. How much is 3 groups of 10?* [30] Write "− 30" below the tens place in the dividend. *Were any tens left?* [No] Write "9" below the "− 30." *Now show me how you divided the ones. How many ones are in each group?* [3] *Since there were 3 ones in each of the 3 groups, we will write a 3 in the ones place of the quotient. How many are in 3 groups of 3?* [9] Write "− 9" below the ones place. *Were any ones left?* [No] Write "0" below the "− 9." *How many patches will Paulo put in each row?* [13 patches]

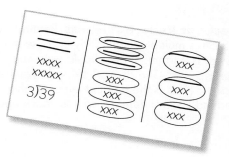

Extend

Harry has 82 quarters. He wants to put them in groups of 4 to count how many dollars he has. Draw a picture to find how many whole dollars Harry has. [He has $20.]

eTools Place-Value Blocks
www.pearsonsuccessnet.com

Visual Learning

Using Objects to Divide: Division as Sharing

How can place value help you divide?

Mrs. Lynch displayed 57 student drawings on 3 walls in her art classroom. If she divided the drawings equally, how many drawings are on each wall?

Estimate: $60 \div 3 = 20$

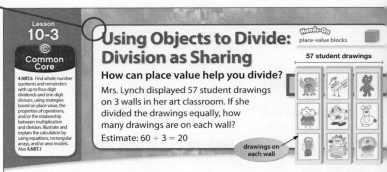

place-value blocks

57 student drawings

drawings on each wall

What fact do you need to divide to find how many drawings are on each wall? [You need to divide 57 by 3.] *Why do you divide 60 by 3 to estimate?* [57 rounds to 60]

Prevent Misconceptions

When students write the number of tens used, make sure they write it below the tens column of the dividend and not below the ones column.

---

1 Visual Learning

Set the Purpose Call students' attention to the **Visual Learning Bridge** at the top of the page. *In this lesson, you will use place value to help you divide.*

Another Example

What are you asked to find? [The number of pieces of paper Helen will fill] *How can you find this?* [By dividing the number of postcards by the number of postcards on each page] *What does the remainder mean?* [It means she has 3 leftover postcards.] *Including the remainder, how many sheets of paper will she use?* [14 sheets]

Explain It

Check for Reasonableness Remind students that the opposite of division is multiplication. They can use multiplication to check if their answer is correct. *What should you multiply the quotient by to check your answer?* [The divisor] *Why do you need to add the remainder back in?* [This is the amount left over after you divide. It is part of the dividend.] *What number do you check against?* [The dividend]

Lesson 10-3

Common Core

4.NBT.6 Find whole-number quotients and remainders with up to four-digit dividends and one-digit divisors, using strategies based on place value, the properties of operations, and/or the relationship between multiplication and division. Illustrate and explain the calculation by using equations, rectangular arrays, and/or area models. Also 4.NBT.1

Using Objects to Divide: Division as Sharing

place-value blocks

57 student drawings

How can place value help you divide?

Mrs. Lynch displayed 57 student drawings on 3 walls in her art classroom. If she divided the drawings equally, how many drawings are on each wall?

Estimate: $60 \div 3 = 20$

drawings on each wall

Another Example How do you model remainders?

Helen has 55 postcards. As an art project, she plans to glue 4 postcards onto sheets of colored paper.

How many pieces of paper can she fill?

Step 1 Divide the tens.

Division is used to find the number of equal groups.

$$\begin{array}{r} 1 \\ 4\overline{)55} \\ -4 \\ \hline 1 \end{array}$$

There is 1 ten in each group and 1 ten left over.

Step 2 Regroup the 1 ten as 10 ones and divide.

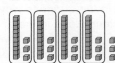

$$\begin{array}{r} 13\,R3 \\ 4\overline{)55} \\ -4 \\ \hline 15 \\ -12 \\ \hline 3 \end{array}$$

Trade the extra ten for ten ones.
15 The 1 ten and 5 ones make 15.
There are 3 ones in each group and 3 left over.

Helen will fill 13 pieces of colored paper.

Explain It

1. In the first step above, what does the 1 in the quotient represent?
1 group of ten or 10

2. **Reasonableness** How can you check that the answer is correct?
Multiply 4×13, then add 3.

232

Visual Learning Animation

Use place-value blocks to show 57.

Divide the tens into three equal groups.

$$3\overline{)57}$$
$$-\,3 \quad \text{3 tens used}$$

Why are only 3 of the 5 tens rods used in this step? [To have three equal groups, there are only enough tens rods to have 1 ten in each group. There are 2 tens rods left over.]

Trade the extra tens for ones.

$$\begin{array}{r} 1 \\ 3\overline{)57} \\ -\,3 \quad \text{3 tens used} \\ \hline 27 \quad \text{27 ones left} \end{array}$$

How do the models show how you traded the 2 extra tens for ones? [The two extra tens rods are replaced by 20 unit cubes.]

Divide the ones.

$$\begin{array}{r} 19 \\ 3\overline{)57} \\ -\,3 \\ \hline 27 \\ -\,27 \quad \text{27 ones used} \\ \hline 0 \end{array}$$

There are 19 drawings on each wall.

What number does each group of place-value blocks show? [19] *What is the quotient?* [19]

Use place-value blocks to show 57.

Divide the tens into three equal groups.

$$3\overline{)57}$$
$$-\,3 \quad \text{3 tens used}$$

Trade the extra tens for ones.

$$\begin{array}{r} 1 \\ 3\overline{)57} \\ -\,3 \quad \text{3 tens used} \\ \hline 27 \quad \text{27 ones left} \end{array}$$

Divide the ones.

$$\begin{array}{r} 19 \\ 3\overline{)57} \\ -\,3 \\ \hline 27 \\ -\,27 \quad \text{27 ones used} \\ \hline 0 \end{array}$$

There are 19 drawings on each wall.

Guided Practice* © MATHEMATICAL PRACTICES

Do you know HOW?

In **1** through **4**, use place-value blocks or draw pictures. Tell how many are in each group and how many are left over.

1. 76 magazines
   5 boxes
   See margin.

2. 56 marbles
   3 bags
   See margin.

3. 82 muffins
   7 boxes
   See margin.

4. 72 photos
   3 albums
   See margin.

Do you UNDERSTAND?

© 5. **Use Tools** Describe another way to show 57 using place-value blocks.
   Sample answer: 57 ones

6. Mrs. Lynch displayed 48 paintings in 3 sets. If each set had the same number of paintings, how many were in each set?
   16 paintings

Independent Practice

Leveled Practice In **7** through **10**, use the model to complete each division sentence.

7. $71 \div \square = \square$ R2 3; 23

8. $\square \div 4 = \square$ 76; 19

9. $\square \div \square = \square$ 85; 5; 17

10. $\square \div \square = \square$ R $\square$ 58; 3; 19; 1

eTools
www.pearsonsuccessnet.com

For another example, see Set C on page 249. Lesson 10-3 **233**

---

2 Guided Practice © MATHEMATICAL PRACTICES

Remind students to break tens rods into ones when needed.

Exercise 3
Error Intervention

If students are having difficulty identifying the number of tens that need to be regrouped as ones,

then ask: *How many tens are in the dividend?* [8] *How many ones are in the dividend?* [2] *How many tens are left over to be regrouped as ones?* [1]

Reteaching For another example and more practice, assign **Reteaching** Set C on p. 249.

3 Independent Practice

Remind students that in order to find the quotient they need to find the value of the place-value blocks in each group. The value of the leftover place-value blocks is the remainder. Use Exercise 7 as an example. *3 sets of 2 tens rods and 3 unit cubes shows 71 divided into 3 equal groups. The divisor is 3. There are 2 tens rods and 3 unit cubes in each group. There are 2 unit cubes left over. This means the quotient is 23 R2.*

---

1. 15 magazines,
   1 left over

2. 18 marbles,
   2 left over

3. 11 muffins,
   5 left over

4. 24 photos,
   0 left over

3 Independent Practice

Encourage students who are having difficulty deciding how many tens to regroup to use place-value blocks to model the problem until they have mastered the concept.

Problem Solving  MATHEMATICAL PRACTICES

Students use underlying processes and mathematical tools for Exercises 31–36. Remind students to check for reasonableness when solving each problem.

Exercise 32

Ⓒ **Communicate** Discuss how using place value will help to determine the number of tens that must be regrouped as ones. Remind students that 64 means that there are 6 tens and 4 ones. When 6 tens are grouped into 4 groups, there is 1 ten in each group with 2 tens left over. These 2 tens need to be regrouped as 20 ones.

Exercise 33

Ⓒ **Use Structure** For multiple-choice items, evaluate the number sentence in each answer choice. Find the one that matches the answer you found to the problem.

Exercise 35

Ⓒ **Persevere in Solving Problems** Review the fact that there are 4 fourth-grade classes on the field trip. Suggest they first find the total number of fourth graders on the trip. *How can you find this number?* [Multiply 4 × 24.] Then point out that the total number of students are being divided into 6 equal groups.

Early Finishers Have students write an explanation for how to determine if any tens will need to be regrouped.

Independent Practice

In **11** through **30**, use place-value blocks or draw pictures to solve.

11. 3)46 — 15 R1
12. 8)96 — 12
13. 4)55 — 13 R3
14. 2)51 — 25 R1
15. 5)89 — 17 R4

16. 6)76 — 12 R4
17. 7)36 — 5 R1
18. 3)72 — 24
19. 2)63 — 31 R1
20. 4)92 — 23

21. 3)44 — 14 R2
22. 4)67 — 16 R3
23. 6)85 — 14 R1
24. 3)56 — 18 R2
25. 5)97 — 19 R2

26. 2)39 — 19 R1
27. 4)31 — 7 R3
28. 5)87 — 17 R2
29. 7)82 — 11 R5
30. 5)22 — 4 R2

Problem Solving MATHEMATICAL PRACTICES

Ⓒ **31. Use Tools** Maya used place-value blocks to divide 86. She made groups of 17 with 1 left over. Use place-value blocks or draw pictures to determine how many groups Maya made.
5 groups

Ⓒ **32. Writing to Explain** Harold has 64 toy cars in 4 equal boxes. To find the number in each box, he divided 64 by 4. How many tens did he regroup as ones?
See margin.

Ⓒ **33. Think About the Structure** Jake walks dogs and delivers papers to earn money. This month, he earned $52 delivering papers and $43 walking dogs. Each month, he puts half of his money into the bank. Which shows how much Jake saved this month?

A (52 + 43) + 2   Ⓒ (52 + 43) ÷ 2
B (52 + 43) × 2   D (52 + 43) − 2

Ⓒ **34. Reason** Tina has 50 berries. She wants to have some each day for lunch. How many berries can she have each day if she wants to eat them all in 5 days?

50 berries

| ? | ? | ? | ? | ? |

↑ number of berries each day
10 berries each day

Ⓒ **35. Persevere** The 4 fourth-grade classes from Jameson Elementary School took a trip to the United States Capitol. Each class had 24 students. At the Capitol, the students were divided into 6 equal groups. How many students were in each group?
16 students

36. A maximum of 40 people are allowed on a tour of the Capitol at one time. After 16 tours, how many people could have gone through the Capitol?
640 people

? people in all

| 40 | 16 tours |

234

---

32. 2 tens as 20 ones; there is one group of 4 in 6 tens with 2 tens left over.

Dividing by Multiples of 10

Patterns can be used when dividing by multiples of 10. It is easy to divide mentally using basic facts and place-value patterns.

Examples:

$7\overline{)21} = 3$

$7\overline{)210} = 30$

$7\overline{)2,100} = 300$

$7\overline{)21,000} = 3,000$

As the number of zeros in the dividend increases, the number of zeros in the quotient increases by the same amount.

$4\overline{)20} = 5$

$40\overline{)200} = 5$

$400\overline{)2,000} = 5$

$4,000\overline{)20,000} = 5$

The number of zeros in the dividend and divisor increase by the same amount, and the quotient remains the same as in the basic fact.

Practice

For **1** through **12**, divide. Use mental math.

1. $30\overline{)90}$
3

2. $90\overline{)6,300}$
70

3. $2\overline{)8,000}$
4,000

4. $900\overline{)4,500}$
5

5. $80\overline{)560}$
7

6. $8\overline{)7,200}$
900

7. $200\overline{)1,400}$
7

8. $70\overline{)4,200}$
60

9. $7\overline{)350}$
50

10. $20\overline{)120}$
6

11. $70\overline{)2,800}$
40

12. $400\overline{)1,600}$
4

13. Reason Write another division problem with the same answer as $90\overline{)3,600}$.
Sample answer: $36,000 \div 900$

14. Use Structure How is dividing 490 by 7 like dividing 49,000 by 700?
Sample answer: $49,000 \div 700$ is the same as 490 hundreds ÷ 7 hundreds, so the quotients are the same.

15. A science museum has 2,400 gemstones displayed equally in 30 cases. How many gemstones are in each case?
80 gemstones

16. Ryan has a collection of 1,800 stickers. He wants to put them in equal groups into 20 sticker albums. How many stickers will be in each album?
90 stickers

Remind students that any multiple of ten can be broken down. For example 20,000 can be expressed as $2 \times 10 \times 10 \times 10 \times 10$. Likewise 4,000 can be expressed as $4 \times 10 \times 10 \times 10$. Then they can divide by simplifying. For example, 20,000 and 4,000 can be simplified to find the basic division problem $20 \div 4$, which is easier to solve.

Exercise 2

Remind students to look for a basic division fact within the problem so they can solve the problem more easily. *Without looking at the zeros, what basic division fact can you use to solve* $6,300 \div 90$? [$63 \div 9 = 7$] *How do you find out how many zeros to put at the end of 7 so you will have your final answer?* [There are 2 zeros in 6,300 and 1 zero in 90. I can eliminate 1 zero in both and put the remaining zero at the end of 7 to get 70.] *How can you double-check your answer?* [Multiply 70 by 90 to get 6,300.]

Exercises 1–12
Error Intervention

If students are having difficulty with larger divisors,

then remind them to use basic facts to help solve the problem.

Exercise 13

 Reason Quantitatively *If you multiplied 3,600 by 10 and 90 by 10, what division problem would you have?* [$36,000 \div 900$] *Why does this problem have the same answer as the original problem?* [Since you're multiplying each number by the same number, when they're divided you'll get the same answer as with the original numbers.]

Close

Essential Understanding The sharing interpretation of division can be used to model the standard division algorithm. *In this lesson, you learned that the tens can be divided into equal groups, trading the extra tens for ones. Then the ones can be divided into equal groups. The sum of the groups is the quotient.*

 ASSESSMENT

Exercises 1 and 2 are worth 1 point each.
Use the rubric to score Exercise 3.

Exercise 3
Writing to Explain Students should identify the relationship between the division problem and the place-value blocks.

ELL Provide a Word List For students who need additional writing support, provide these words to help them in their answers:

Divisor   Dividend   Quotient   Remainder

Student Samples
3-point answer The student writes a division sentence which is correct. The explanation demonstrates complete knowledge of two-digit quotients and how the model relates to the problem.

> Add all of the blocks to find the first number.
> 20 + 2 + 20 + 2 + 20 + 2 + 20 + 2 + 3 = 91
> You divide by the number of groups, 4.
> 91 ÷ 4 = 22 R3
> Each group has 20 + 2 = 22, and there are 3 leftover blocks.

2-point answer The division sentence is correct, but the student provides no explanation.

> 91 ÷ 4 = 22 R3

1-point answer The student's division sentence is incorrect. The explanation shows little understanding of connecting division and models.

> 90 ÷ 4 = 25
> I counted the blocks in the groups. I got 90. There are 4 groups. I counted the blocks in each group. There are 22. Then I added the leftover. I got 25.

Prescription for Differentiated Instruction
Use student work on the **Quick Check** to prescribe differentiated instruction.

Points	Prescription
0–2	**Intervention**
3–4	**On-Level**
5	**Advanced**

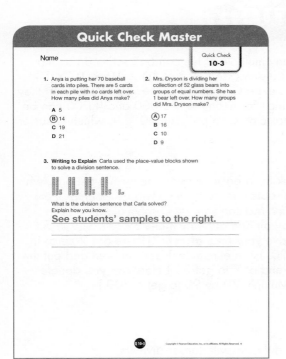

Quick Check Master

Name _____   Quick Check 10-3

1. Anya is putting her 70 baseball cards into piles. There are 5 cards in each pile with no cards left over. How many piles did Anya make?
   A 5
   B 14
   C 19
   D 21

2. Mrs. Dryson is dividing her collection of 52 glass bears into groups of equal numbers. She has 1 bear left over. How many groups did Mrs. Dryson make?
   A 17
   B 16
   C 10
   D 9

3. **Writing to Explain** Carla used the place-value blocks shown to solve a division sentence.

What is the division sentence that Carla solved? Explain how you know.
See students' samples to the right.

 **Formative** Assessment

Use the **Quick Check** to assess students' understanding.

Differentiated Instruction

Intervention

Using Objects to Divide: Division as Sharing

 10–15 min

Materials Place-value blocks (Teaching Tool 8)

- Have students solve 49 ÷ 3 using place-value blocks.
- Have students place 4 tens rods and 9 unit cubes in their workspace. *How could we show dividing by 3?* [Divide the blocks into 3 groups.]
- Have students move the tens rods so there are three groups with 1 rod in each group. *How many tens rods are left over?* [1]
- Have students trade the tens rod for 10 ones cubes. *How many ones cubes are there now?* [19] Have students move the cubes into the groups. *How many cubes are left over?* [1] This is the remainder.

On-Level

Practice · **Center Activity**

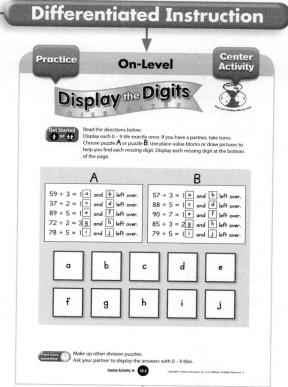

Advanced

Practice · **Center Activity**

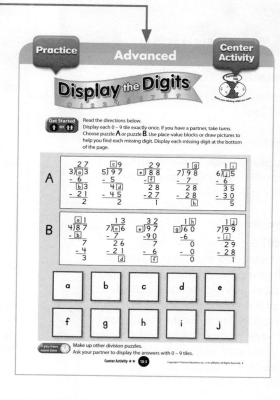

ELL Report Back To check understanding, ask a student to repeat and complete this sentence: *To divide 89 by 5, we find out how many tens we can put in each of the five groups, and then we trade 3 tens for 30 ones and we _____.* [share the ones]

Leveled Homework

Reteaching Master

Also available in print

Practice Master

Also available in print

Enrichment Master

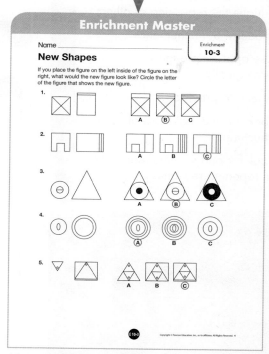

Also available in print

Dividing 2-Digit by 1-Digit Numbers

 **Lesson Overview**

Domain

Number and Operations in Base Ten

Cluster

Use place value understanding and properties of operations to perform multi-digit arithmetic.

Standard

4.NBT.6 Find whole-number quotients and remainders with up to four-digit dividends and one-digit divisors, using strategies based on place value, the properties of operations, and/or the relationship between multiplication and division. Illustrate and explain the calculation by using equations, rectangular arrays, and/or area models.

Mathematical Practices

☑ Make sense of problems and persevere in solving them.

☑ Reason abstractly and quantitatively.

☑ Construct viable arguments and critique the reasoning of others.

○ Model with mathematics.

○ Use appropriate tools strategically.

○ Attend to precision.

○ Look for and make use of structure.

☑ Look for and express regularity in repeated reasoning.

Objective	Essential Understanding	Vocabulary	Materials
Students will use the standard algorithm to divide a two-digit number by a one-digit number.	The standard division algorithm breaks the calculation into simpler calculations using basic facts, place-value, the relationship between multiplication and division, and estimation.		

 PROFESSIONAL DEVELOPMENT

Math Background

Research says ... learning new mathematical procedures can be enhanced by analyzing the procedure, breaking it down into its component parts, and providing instruction on each component (Gagne, 1977; Dick & Carey, 1996). In this lesson, students will use algorithms for long division.

The example at the top of pp. 236–237 shows each component of long division.

Component Part I: Think of the 76 as 7 tens and 6 ones. The tens are broken into four equal groups. Each group receives 1 ten,

hence the 1 ten in the quotient. Four tens have been used up, leaving 3 remaining, or $7 - 4 = 3$.

$$\begin{array}{r} 19 \\ 4\overline{)76} \\ -4 \\ \hline 36 \\ -36 \\ \hline 0 \end{array}$$

Component Part II: The three remaining tens are then regrouped into ones and combined with the remaining ones. Now, bring the six down. The 36 is 36 ones.

Component Part III: The 36 ones are broken into four equal groups. Each group receives 9 ones, hence the 9 ones in the quotient. All 36 ones have been used up, leaving 0 remaining.

1 Daily Common Core Review

Daily Common Core Review

Name _____

Daily Common Core Review **10-4**

1. The Smith family is packing to move. Each moving box holds 30 glasses. There are 94 glasses and 3 boxes. How many extra glasses are there?
   (A) 4
   B 3
   C 2
   D 1

2. Samantha drives 95 miles each day. How many miles does she drive in 40 days?
   A 2,800 miles
   B 3,400 miles
   (C) 3,800 miles
   D 4,800 miles

3. Antonio runs 4 miles each day. How many miles does he run in three months? Remember, one month has 30 days.
   A 260 miles
   B 300 miles
   (C) 360 miles
   D 400 miles

4. Lola is planning a surprise party for her brother. She is inviting 36 people besides her brother and herself. She can seat 6 people at each table. How many tables will Lola need?
   A 5
   B 6
   (C) 7
   D 8

5. Joe does 25 sit-ups each day. How many sit-ups does he do in 3 weeks? Remember, one week has 7 days.
   525 sit-ups

6. **Estimation** Estimate the quotient.
   $555 \div 8$
   70

7. Multiply.
   $\begin{array}{r} 37 \\ \times\ 32 \\ \hline 1{,}184 \end{array}$

Content Reviewed

Exercise 1   Remainders

Exercise 2   Multiplication

Exercise 3   Multiplication

Exercise 4   Division

Exercise 5   Multi-Step Problems

Exercise 6   Estimate Division

Exercise 7   Multiplication

Also available in print

 10–15 min # Problem-Based Interactive Learning

Overview Students will use the division algorithm to divide.

Focus What is a common way to record division?

 **Set the Purpose** *You have already learned to model division using place-value blocks and to record your work. Today, you will be learning how to use a common way to record division.*

Connect Point out that division of 2-digit numbers can be seen in everyday life. *When the class splits into equal groups to work or you share a large box of crayons equally, you are dividing a 2-digit number.*

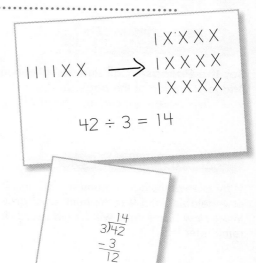

MATHEMATICAL PRACTICES

Make Generalizations When students use the division algorithm to divide, they make generalizations.

Pose the Problem *Swati is packing T-shirts and shorts into boxes to put away for the winter. There are 42 items to pack. She packs the same number of items into 3 boxes. How many items does Swati pack in each box?* Allow pairs of students to work together to solve and record this problem. Then have them share their solutions with the class.

Model and Discuss Help students learn to record their actions. Write 3)42. *How many tens can go in each group?* [1] Write 1 in the tens place of the quotient. *Are there any tens remaining?* [Yes, there will be 1 ten remaining.] Show the ten that is left as a subtraction. *How many items are left?* [12] Write the 2 next to the 1 ten that is left. *How many items can you put in each group?* [4] *Are there any leftovers?* [No, there are 14 items in each box.]

Small-Group Interaction *Work with your partner. Divide 85 by 5. Follow the steps you used to solve the problem. As you divide, explain your work to your partner. Reverse roles and repeat to divide 87 by 3.*

 Suppose Emma had 62 items to pack into 4 boxes. If she packed the same number of items in each box, would she have any items left over? Explain. [Yes, 62 ÷ 4 = 15 with 2 left over.]

Visual Learning

Dividing 2-Digit by 1-Digit Numbers

What is a common way to record division?

At the school food drive, Al needs to put the same number of soup cans into four boxes. How many soup cans will go in each box?

Choose an Operation Divide to find the number in each group.

76 cans of soup in all

What information are you given in this problem? [Al has 76 soup cans and four boxes.] *What must you do to solve the problem?* [Divide 76 by 4 to find how many soup cans Al puts in each box.]

---

1 Visual Learning

Set the Purpose Call students' attention to the **Visual Learning Bridge** at the top of the page. *In this lesson, you will keep track of your division using a common record keeping method.*

Another Example

Why are you using the numbers 58 and 4? [58 is the number of cans of vegetables and 4 is the number of groups the cans will be broken into.] *How many cans will be left over? How do you know?* [2; the remainder is 2.]

Explain It

© **Check for Reasonableness** Remind students to use compatible numbers when estimating division. *What numbers close to 58 and 4 are compatible?* [60 and 4] *Why are 60 and 4 considered compatible?* [The division can be completed mentally.]

Lesson 10-4

© **Common Core**

4.NBT.6 Find whole-number quotients and remainders with up to four-digit dividends and one-digit divisors, using strategies based on place value, the properties of operations, and/or the relationship between multiplication and division. Illustrate and explain the calculation by using equations, rectangular arrays, and/or area models.

Dividing 2-Digit by 1-Digit Numbers

76 cans of soup in all

What is a common way to record division?

At the school food drive, Al needs to put the same number of soup cans into four boxes. How many soup cans will go in each box?

Choose an Operation Divide to find the number in each group.

Another Example | How do you divide with a remainder?

Al collects 58 cans of vegetables. He puts the same number of cans in four boxes. How many cans of vegetables will go in each box? How many cans will be left over?

A 14 cans, 2 cans left over

B 15 cans, 2 cans left over

C 16 cans, 2 cans left over

D 18 cans, 2 cans left over

Step 1	**Step 2**	**Step 3**
Divide the tens.	Divide the ones.	Check: $14 \times 4 = 56$ and $56 + 2 = 58$.
Regroup the remaining ten as 10 ones.	Subtract to find the remainder.	There will be 14 cans of vegetables in each box and 2 cans left over.
$\begin{array}{r} 1 \\ 4\overline{)58} \\ -4 \\ \hline 1 \end{array}$	$\begin{array}{r} 14 \\ 4\overline{)58} \\ -4 \\ \hline 18 \\ -16 \\ \hline 2 \end{array}$	The correct choice is **A**.

Explain It

© **1. Reasonableness** How can you use estimation to decide if 14 cans is reasonable? 58 is close to 60 and $60 \div 4$ is 15. Since 14 is close to 15, the answer is reasonable.

2. Why is multiplication used to check division?
Multiplication and division have an inverse relationship.

236

Step 1

Divide the tens.

$$\begin{array}{r} 1 \\ 4{\overline{\smash{\big)}\,76}} \\ -4 \\ \hline 3 \end{array}$$

Think There is 1 ten in each group and 3 tens left over.

Why is there only 1 ten in each group? [To have 4 equal groups, there are only enough tens to have 1 in each group.]

Step 2

Divide the ones.

$$\begin{array}{r} 19 \\ 4{\overline{\smash{\big)}\,76}} \\ -4 \\ \hline 36 \\ -36 \\ \hline 0 \end{array}$$

Think Trade the 3 tens for 30 ones. 30 ones and 6 ones make 36 ones.

There will be 19 soup cans in each box.

Why can you trade 3 tens for 30 ones? [1 ten can be traded for 10 ones, so 3 tens can be traded for 30 ones, because $3 \times 10 = 30$.]

Step 3

Check by multiplying.

$$\begin{array}{r} 3 \\ 19 \\ \times\; 4 \\ \hline 76 \end{array}$$

The answer checks.

What parts of a division problem do you multiply to check division? [Multiply the quotient by the divisor.]

Step 1

Divide the tens.

$$\begin{array}{r} 1 \\ 4{\overline{\smash{\big)}\,76}} \\ -4 \\ \hline 3 \end{array}$$

Think There is 1 ten in each group and 3 tens left over.

Step 2

Divide the ones.

$$\begin{array}{r} 19 \\ 4{\overline{\smash{\big)}\,76}} \\ -4 \\ \hline 36 \\ -36 \\ \hline 0 \end{array}$$

Think Trade the 3 tens for 30 ones. 30 ones and 6 ones make 36 ones.

There will be 19 soup cans in each box.

Step 3

Check by multiplying.

$$\begin{array}{r} 3 \\ 19 \\ \times\; 4 \\ \hline 76 \end{array}$$

The answer checks.

Guided Practice*    MATHEMATICAL PRACTICES

Do you know HOW?

In **1** and **2**, copy and complete each calculation.

1.
$$\begin{array}{r} 4\;\; 7 \\ 2{\overline{\smash{\big)}\,94}} \\ -\;8 \\ \hline \quad 4\;1 \\ -1\;\;4 \\ \hline 0 \end{array}$$

2.
$$\begin{array}{r} 1\;6R\;2 \\ 5{\overline{\smash{\big)}\,82}} \\ -\;5 \\ \hline \quad 32 \\ -\quad 30 \\ \hline 2 \end{array}$$

Do you UNDERSTAND?

3. **Communicate** Explain how you would estimate the answer in Exercise 2.
See margin.

4. Al collects 85 cans of fruit. He puts the same number of fruit cans in 4 boxes. Will he have any cans left over? If so, how many cans?
Yes; 1 can

Independent Practice

Leveled Practice In **5** through **8**, copy and complete each calculation. Estimate to check reasonableness.

5.
$$\begin{array}{r} \;\;12 \\ 7{\overline{\smash{\big)}\,84}} \\ -\;7 \\ \hline \quad 4\;1 \\ -\;\;14 \\ \hline 0 \end{array}$$

6.
$$\begin{array}{r} \;6\;2 \\ 3{\overline{\smash{\big)}\,78}} \\ -\;6 \\ \hline 8\;1 \\ -1\;\;8 \\ \hline 0 \end{array}$$

7.
$$\begin{array}{r} 23\;\;R\;1 \\ 4{\overline{\smash{\big)}\,93}} \\ -\;8 \\ \hline 13 \\ -1\;2 \\ \hline 1 \end{array}$$

8.
$$\begin{array}{r} 1\;R\;3\;\;2 \\ 6{\overline{\smash{\big)}\,80}} \\ -\;6 \\ \hline 20 \\ -1\;8 \\ \hline 2 \end{array}$$

For **9** through **18**, find each quotient. Use multiplication to check.

9. $3{\overline{\smash{\big)}\,63}}$
21

10. $7{\overline{\smash{\big)}\,88}}$
12 R4

11. $6{\overline{\smash{\big)}\,96}}$
16

12. $4{\overline{\smash{\big)}\,52}}$
13

13. $5{\overline{\smash{\big)}\,73}}$
14 R3

14. $5{\overline{\smash{\big)}\,93}}$
18 R3

15. $3{\overline{\smash{\big)}\,87}}$
29

16. $4{\overline{\smash{\big)}\,72}}$
18

17. $6{\overline{\smash{\big)}\,77}}$
12 R5

18. $2{\overline{\smash{\big)}\,37}}$
18 R1

For another example, see Set D on page 249.

Lesson 10-4   **237**

---

2 **Guided Practice**    MATHEMATICAL PRACTICES

Remind students that this lesson is showing them how to keep track of the division they learned in Lesson 10-3.

Exercise 2
Error Intervention

If students are having difficulty dividing the first digit of the dividend,

then ask: *What does the 8 represent in the 82?* [8 tens] *How many tens will be in each group if there are 5 groups?* [1] *How many tens are left over?* [3]

Reteaching For another example and more practice, assign **Reteaching** Set D on p. 249.

3 **Independent Practice**

Remind students to use what they learned about place-value blocks to help them divide using the algorithm. Use Exercise 5 as an example. *There are 8 tens rods and 4 ones cubes. If the tens rods are sorted into 7 groups, there is 1 rod in each group. The tens digit of the quotient is 1. There is 1 rod left over. When the tens digits are subtracted the difference is 1. When the 4 is written next to the leftover tens, it is the same as regrouping the 1 ten and 4 ones as 14 ones. There are 2 groups of 7 in 14 ones. The ones digit of the quotient is 2.*

3. Round 82 to 80 and divide by 5.

237

3 Independent Practice

Remind students to estimate before they divide. Students should use their estimates to check for reasonableness.

Problem Solving © MATHEMATICAL PRACTICES

Students use underlying processes and mathematical tools for Exercises 29–36. Remind students to check for reasonableness when solving each problem.

Exercise 33

© **Construct Arguments** Estimation can be used to find the number of digits in the quotient. 40 ÷ 4 = 10. Any dividend greater than 40 will create a two-digit quotient. Therefore, 51 ÷ 4 will have a two-digit quotient. 60 ÷ 6 = 10. Any dividend less than 60 will have a one-digit quotient. Therefore, 51 ÷ 6 will have a one-digit quotient.

Exercise 35

© **Persevere in Solving Problems** For multiple-choice items, eliminate answer choices that do not make sense. Answer choices A and D are not the closest answer choices to the original dividend of 78.

Early Finishers Have students write and solve a new problem using the recipe with 31 and 32.

Independent Practice

In **19** through **28**, find each quotient. Use multiplication to check.

19. 3)46 — 15 R1 **20.** 7)65 — 9 R2 **21.** 8)27 — 3 R3 **22.** 9)86 — 9 R5 **23.** 4)66 — 16 R2

24. 8)59 — 7 R3 **25.** 4)92 — 23 **26.** 3)74 — 24 R2 **27.** 5)68 — 13 R3 **28.** 2)89 — 44 R1

Problem Solving © MATHEMATICAL PRACTICES

© **29. Reason** Some of the tallest selenite crystals in a cave in Chihuahua, Mexico, are 50 feet tall. About how many times taller are the tallest crystals than a 4-foot-tall fourth grader?
12 or 13 times taller

30. Zelda has a piece of fabric that is 74 inches long. She wants to divide it into 2 equal pieces. What is the length of each piece?
37 inches

Use the recipe at the right for **31** and **32**.

31. How many ounces of Tasty Trail Mix are made from the recipe?
18 ounces

32. Maggie is making trail mix. She makes 4 batches of the recipe shown. Then she divides it into 3 equal sized bags. How many ounces are in each bag?
24 ounces

Tasty Trail Mix	
Granola	8 oz
Nuts	5 oz
Raisins	2 oz
Cranberries	3 oz

© **33. Writing to Explain** Why does 51 ÷ 4 have two digits in the quotient, while 51 ÷ 6 has only one digit in the quotient?
See margin.

© **34. Write a Problem** Write a problem that could be solved by dividing 78 by 5.
See margin.

© **35. Persevere** Paulo has 78 cattle on his ranch. He needs to divide them equally among 3 pastures. Which shows the best way to estimate the number of cattle in each pasture?

A 60 ÷ 3 © 75 ÷ 3
B 66 ÷ 3 D 90 ÷ 3

36. Every year, the city of San Marcos holds a Cinco de Mayo festival. If 60 students perform in 5 equal groups, how many students are in each group?

A 10 students C 25 students
B 12 students D 55 students

---

33. In 51 ÷ 4, there is 1 group of 4 in 5 tens. So, you can divide both the tens and the ones, giving a two-digit quotient. In 51 ÷ 6, there are no groups of 6 in 5 tens. The tens must be regrouped as ones and divided, giving a one-digit quotient.

34. Sample answer: Juana has a ribbon that is 78 inches long. She wants to divide it into 5 equal whole-inch pieces. How long will each piece be? [15 inches with 3 inches left over]

Venn Diagrams

A **Venn diagram** is a diagram that uses circles to show the relationships between groups of data. When the circles overlap, or **intersect**, the data belong to more than one group.

Example: Robin, Kevin, and Coreen are in the Math Club.

Sara, Callie, Mike, Brad, and Rachel are in the Science Club.

Gwen and Dan are in both clubs.

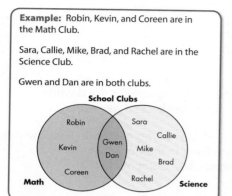

School Clubs

Math | Science
Robin, Kevin, Coreen | Gwen, Dan | Sara, Callie, Mike, Brad, Rachel

---

Practice

For **1** through **3**, use the Venn diagram to the right.

1. To which group does 24 belong?
   Multiples of 3
2. Which numbers are multiples of both 3 and 5?
   15 and 30
3. In which part of the Venn diagram would you place 48? 50? 60?
   Multiples of 3; Multiples of 5, Intersecting part

For **4** through **6**, use the Venn diagram to the right.

4. Which factors of 16 are also factors of 48?
   1, 2, 4, 8, 16
5. Which factors of 48 are not factors of 16 and 40?
   3, 6, 12, 24, 48
6. Which numbers are factors of 16, 40, and 48?
   1, 2, 4, 8
7. Make a Venn diagram that uses two circles.
8. Make a Venn diagram that uses three circles.
   For 7–8, check students' work.

Multiples of 3 and 5 to 40

3   9
33
6
18   15
12   30
39   24
21
36   27
3

5   10
20
25   35
40
5

Factors of 16, 40, and 48

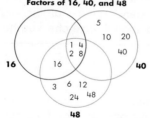

5
10   20
40
1   4
2   8
16   16   **40**
3   6   12
24   48
48

Enrichment

Point out to students that diagrams can help them see and compare data quickly. Venn diagrams are used to compare data about two or more groups at the same time.

Exercise 1

Remind students that the label underneath each circle describes the data in that circle. *What label is under the circle on the left?* [3] *What does that mean?* [All the numbers in the circle on the left are multiples of 3.]

Exercises 1–8
Error Intervention

If students are having difficulty using the Venn diagrams,

then remind students that the intersecting parts show data that is in two or more groups.

Close

Essential Understanding The standard division algorithm breaks the calculation into simpler calculations using basic facts, place-value, the relationship between multiplication and division, and estimation. *In this lesson, you learned how to use division and subtraction in an algorithm to divide.*

Quick Check Master

Name _____

Quick Check 10-4

1. Mark is reading a book with 96 pages. It takes him 4 days to read the book. He reads the same number of pages each day. How many pages does Mark read each day?

A 14
B 18
(C) 24
D 28

2. Celia has 83 beads. She makes 6 bracelets and uses the same number of beads for each bracelet. How many beads does Celia have left over?

(A) 5
B 4
C 3
D 0

3. **Writing to Explain** Jessica solved the division problem as shown.

```
      13
  7 )95
    - 7
     25
    -21
      4
```
The answer is 17.

Is her answer correct? If not, what did Jessica do wrong? How could she have checked her work?
<u>See students' samples to the right.</u>

10-4   Copyright © Pearson Education, Inc., or its affiliates. All Rights Reserved. 4

Formative Assessment

Use the **Quick Check** to assess students' understanding.

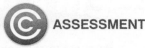
ASSESSMENT

Exercises 1 and 2 are worth 1 point each. Use the rubric to score Exercise 3.

Exercise 3

Writing to Explain Students should find the error in the division problem and state how Jessica should have checked her work.

ELL Provide a Word List For students who need additional writing support, provide these words to help them in their answers: *Divisor Dividend Quotient Remainder Compatible*

Student Samples
3-point answer The student identifies the answer as incorrect and provides an explanation to describe what Jessica did wrong. The student also provides an explanation exhibiting a complete knowledge of dividing and how to check his/her work.

> She's wrong. She added the 4 to the answer. The 4 is the remainder. The answer should be 13 R4. She could have multiplied to check.
> 13 × 7 = 91,
> 91 + 4 = 95.

2-point answer The student identifies the answer as incorrect, but provides no explanation. The student provides an incomplete explanation to describe how Jessica should have checked her work.

> Wrong. Multiply the right answer by 7.

1-point answer The student identifies the answer as incorrect, but provides no explanation or an explanation that does not show an understanding of division.

> She was wrong. There were more groups than Jessica said. She should have checked her work.

Prescription for Differentiated Instruction
Use student work on the **Quick Check** to prescribe differentiated instruction.

Points	Prescription
0–2	Intervention
3–4	On-Level
5	Advanced

Differentiated Instruction

Intervention

Dividing 2-Digit by 1-Digit Numbers

🕐 10–15 min 👥

Materials Place-value blocks (Teaching Tool 8)

- Have students solve 68 ÷ 4 using 6 tens rods and 8 unit cubes.
- *How could we show dividing by 4?* [Divide blocks into 4 groups.] Write the problem using long division.
- Have students make four groups with 1 rod in each group. *How many tens are in each group?* [1] Write 1 in the tens place of the quotient. *How many tens rods are left over?* [2]
- Have students trade the 2 tens rods for 20 ones cubes.
- Have students move the 28 cubes into the four equal groups. *How many cubes are left over?* [0]

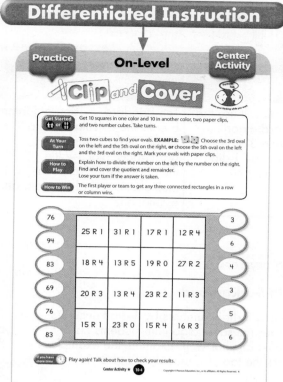

Practice / On-Level / Center Activity — Clip and Cover

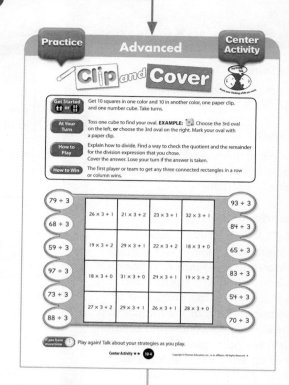

Practice / Advanced / Center Activity — Clip and Cover

ELL Partner Talk Listen for evidence that a student understands how to check a quotient. A student might say, "When I multiply the quotient by the divisor, I do not get the number I am dividing unless I add the remainder."

Leveled Homework

Reteaching Master

Name _____

Dividing 2-Digit by 1-Digit Numbers

Reteaching 10-4

You can find 2-digit quotients by breaking apart the problem and dividing tens, then ones.

Find 85 ÷ 5.
Estimate: 100 ÷ 5 = 20.
17
5)85
−5
35
−35
0
Check: 17 × 5 = 85.
The answer checks.

Find 55 ÷ 3.
Estimate: 60 ÷ 3 = 20.
18 R1
3)55
−3
25
−24
1
Check: 18 × 3 = 54.
54 + 1 = 55
The answer checks.

Find 83 ÷ 7.
Estimate: 84 ÷ 7 = 12.
11 R6
7)83
−7
13
−7
6
Check: 11 × 7 = 77.
77 + 6 = 83
The answer checks.

Find the missing values.

1. 30 R1 — 3)91
2. 21 R2 — 4)86
37 R1 — 2)75

3. 30 R1 4. 21 R2 5. 37 R1

Also available in print

Practice Master

Name _____

Dividing 2-Digit by 1-Digit Numbers

Practice 10-4

1. 2 8 / 3)8 4
2. 1 1 R4 / 6)7 0
3. 1 8 / 4)7 2

4. 36 / 2)72
5. 17 R1 / 5)86
6. 13 R3 / 7)94
7. 13 / 3)39

8. 12 R3 / 8)99
9. 17 R2 / 5)87
10. 48 / 2)96
11. 14 R1 / 3)43

Mrs. Thomas is planning to provide snacks for 96 fourth graders when they go on a field trip to the aquarium. Each student will receive 1 of each snack. Using the bar graph to the right, how many packages of each snack does Mrs. Thomas need?

12. fruit cups — **24 packages**
13. applesauce — **16 packages**

14. Which is the remainder of 27 ÷ 4?
A 1 B 2 (C) 3 D 4

15. **Writing to Explain** Explain how to find the number of leftover pencils if Wendy wants to share 37 pencils with 9 people.

Sample answer: Wendy will give each person 4 pencils and have 1 left over.
37 ÷ 9 = 4 R1

Also available in print

Enrichment Master

Name _____

Will They Reach the Top?

Enrichment 10-4

Begin at the bottom of each mountain and solve each division problem. If there is a remainder, the hiker stops at that problem. If there is no remainder, the hiker keeps climbing.

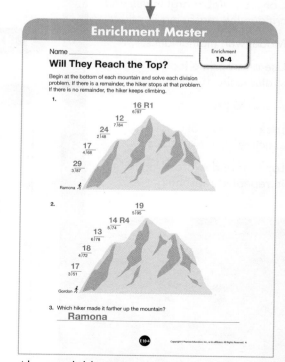

1. 16 R1 / 7)97
12 / 7)84
24 / 2)48
17 / 4)68
29 / 3)87
Ramona

2. 19 / 5)95
14 R4 / 5)74
13 / 6)78
18 / 4)72
17 / 3)51
Gordon

3. Which hiker made it farther up the mountain?
Ramona

Also available in print

Domain

Number and Operations in Base Ten

Cluster

Use place value understanding and properties of operations to perform multi-digit arithmetic.

Standard

4.NBT.6 Find whole-number quotients and remainders with up to four-digit dividends and one-digit divisors, using strategies based on place value, the properties of operations, and/or the relationship between multiplication and division. Illustrate and explain the calculation by using equations, rectangular arrays, and/or area models.

Mathematical Practices

✔ Make sense of problems and persevere in solving them.

✔ Reason abstractly and quantitatively.

✔ Construct viable arguments and critique the reasoning of others.

○ Model with mathematics.

○ Use appropriate tools strategically.

○ Attend to precision.

○ Look for and make use of structure.

✔ Look for and express regularity in repeated reasoning.

Dividing 3-Digit by 1-Digit Numbers

Lesson Overview

Objective	Essential Understanding	Vocabulary	Materials
Students will use the standard algorithm to divide 3-digit numbers by 1-digit numbers.	The standard division algorithm breaks the calculation into simpler calculations using basic facts, place-value, the relationship between multiplication and division, and estimation.		

PROFESSIONAL DEVELOPMENT

Math Background

Dividing 3-digit numbers by 1-digit numbers involves the same algorithm students have become familiar with. Examine the example across the top of pages 240 and 241.

Write 37 divided by 3 on the board. Students are already familiar with dividing a 2-digit number by a 1-digit divisor.

$$\begin{array}{r} 12 \\ 3\overline{)37} \\ -3 \\ \hline 7 \\ -6 \\ \hline 1 \end{array}$$

Comparing this to the division problem at the right, we can see that the steps for solving $37 \div 3$ are the beginning steps to solving $378 \div 3$. The 3-digit dividend requires more steps to solve.

$$\begin{array}{r} 126 \\ 3\overline{)378} \\ -3 \\ \hline 7 \\ -6 \\ \hline 18 \\ -18 \\ \hline 0 \end{array}$$

1 Daily Common Core Review

Daily Common Core Review

Name _____

Daily Common Core Review
10-5

1. Nola earns $62 per week walking dogs. How much money does Nola make in one year? Remember, one year has 52 weeks.
   A $3,442
   B $3,224
   C $3,124
   D $2,134

2. **Mental Math** Seven students are planning to take an exercise class. If the cost is $9 per student, how much will all the students pay for one class?
   A $80
   B $72
   C $63
   D $56

3. Benny has 79 sports cards. He wants to give them to 4 of his friends. He wants each friend to have an equal number of cards. How many sports cards will Benny have left over?
   A 0
   B 1
   C 2
   D 3

4. Kelly needs to buy 2 front row tickets for $35 each and 2 bleacher tickets for $15 each. How much money will she spend on tickets?
   $100

5. Scott has $49 and would like to buy some model cars. Each model car costs $9. How many model cars can he buy? How much more money will he need to buy another model car?
   He can buy 5; he needs another $5 to buy another model car.

6. Round 9,870 to the nearest hundred.
   9,900

Content Reviewed

Exercise 1   Multiplication

Exercise 2   Multiplication

Exercise 3   Interpret Remainder

Exercise 4   Multi-Step Problems

Exercise 5   Division

Exercise 6   Rounding Whole Numbers

Also available in print

 **10–15 min** # Problem-Based Interactive Learning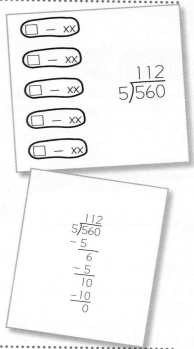

Overview Students will learn to divide 3-digit numbers by 1-digit numbers.

Focus How can you divide numbers in the hundreds?

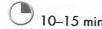 **Set the Purpose** *You have learned to divide 2-digit numbers. Today, you will learn how to divide 3-digit numbers.*

Connect *What are the steps to dividing a 2-digit number?* [Start dividing the tens, and then the ones. Record any remainders.]

 **MATHEMATICAL PRACTICES**

Make Generalizations When students apply the division algorithm used for 2-digit numbers to 3-digit numbers, they make generalizations.

Pose the Problem *The local elementary school has 560 students. All 5 grades have the same number of students. How many students are in each grade?* Have students work in pairs to solve the problem. Encourage them to draw their solutions.

Instruct in Small Steps Once pairs have discussed their own solutions to the problem, work through the problem as a class. Write 5)560 on the board. *How can you solve the problem?* [Divide 560 by 5.] *Dividing a 3-digit number follows the same procedure as dividing a 2-digit number.* Work through the algorithm with students. *What do you divide first?* [The hundreds] *How many hundreds are in each group? Are there any hundreds remaining?* [1 hundred; No hundreds remain.] *What is the next step?* [Divide the tens.] *How many tens go in each group? Are there any tens remaining?* [1 ten; 1 ten remains] *What do you do with the remaining ten?* [Trade it for 10 ones.] *How many ones go in each group? Are there any ones remaining?* [2; No ones remain.] *How many students are in each grade?* [112 students]

Small-Group Interaction Have students work in pairs to record 324 divided by 6.

 Explain the steps you would use to solve the problem 434 divided by 2. You can use drawings to help explain. [Check students' work.]

Visual Learning

Dividing 3-Digit by 1-Digit Numbers

How can you divide numbers in the hundreds?

A factory shipped 378 watches in 3 boxes. If the watches were equally divided, how many watches were there in each box?

Choose an Operation Divide to find the number in each group.

378 watches

↑ watches in each box

What information are you given? [There are 378 watches, and the same number of watches were put into each of the 3 boxes.] *What do you need to divide to find how many watches were in each box?* [Divide 378 by 3.]

Estimate:
$360 \div 3 = 120$
Divide the hundreds.

$$\begin{array}{r} 1 \\ 3\overline{)378} \\ -\,3 \\ \hline 7 \end{array}$$

---

1 Visual Learning

Set the Purpose Call students' attention to the **Visual Learning Bridge** at the top of the page. *In this lesson, you will divide 3-digit numbers by 1-digit numbers.*

2 Guided Practice ⓒ MATHEMATICAL PRACTICES

The algorithm used to divide 2-digit numbers by 1-digit divisors can be applied to divide 3-digit numbers by 1-digit divisors.

Exercise 3
Error Intervention

If students are having difficulty understanding the value of the 1 in the quotient,

then ask: *How many boxes are the 378 watches going into?* [3] *When you divide 378 by 3, what do you get?* [126] *The 1 represents 1 hundred.*

Reteaching Model dividing a 3-digit number by a 1-digit divisor, such as $725 \div 6$. For another example and more practice, assign **Reteaching** Set E on p. 250.

3 Independent Practice

Students may have difficulty recognizing $952 \div 4$ is the same as $4\overline{)952}$. Use Exercise 9 as an example. *You are dividing 952 by 4. The divisor is 4; this is the number to the left of the long division sign. The dividend is 952; this is the number under the division sign.*

Lesson 10-5

ⓒ Common Core

4.NBT.6 Find whole-number quotients and remainders with up to four-digit dividends and one-digit divisors, using strategies based on place value, the properties of operations, and/or the relationship between multiplication and division. Illustrate and explain the calculation by using equations, rectangular arrays, and/or area models.

Dividing 3-Digit by 1-Digit Numbers

How can you divide numbers in the hundreds?

A factory shipped 378 watches in 3 boxes. If the watches were equally divided, how many watches were there in each box?

Choose an Operation Divide to find the number in each group.

378 watches

watches in each box

Guided Practice* ⓒ MATHEMATICAL PRACTICES

Do you know HOW?

In **1** and **2**, copy and complete each calculation.

1.
$$\begin{array}{r} 3\,\blacksquare\,29 \\ 2\overline{)658} \\ -\,6 \\ \hline 5 \\ -\,4 \\ \hline 18 \\ -\,18 \\ \hline 0 \end{array}$$

2. R 238; 2
$$\begin{array}{r} \blacksquare\,R\,238;\,2 \\ 4\overline{)954} \\ -\,8 \\ \hline 15 \\ -\,12 \\ \hline 34 \\ -\,32 \\ \hline 2 \end{array}$$

Do you UNDERSTAND?

ⓒ **3. Persevere** When you divide the hundreds in the problem above, what does the 1 in the quotient represent?
1 hundred

4. Jenny paid $195 to take violin lessons for 3 months. How much did 1 month of lessons cost?
$65

$195

| ? | ? | ? |

↑ Cost for 1 month

Independent Practice

Leveled Practice In **5** through **13**, divide. You may draw a picture to help you.

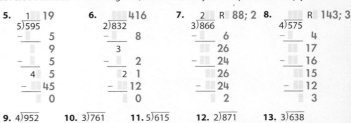

5.
$$\begin{array}{r} 1\,\blacksquare\,19 \\ 5\overline{)595} \\ -\,5 \\ \hline 9 \\ -\,5 \\ \hline 4\quad5 \\ -\,45 \\ \hline 0 \end{array}$$

6.
$$\begin{array}{r} \blacksquare\blacksquare\,416 \\ 2\overline{)832} \\ -\,8 \\ \hline 3 \\ -\,2 \\ \hline 2\quad1 \\ -\,12 \\ \hline 0 \end{array}$$

7. R 88; 2
$$\begin{array}{r} 2\,\blacksquare\,R\,88;\,2 \\ 3\overline{)866} \\ -\,6 \\ \hline 26 \\ -\,24 \\ \hline 26 \\ -\,24 \\ \hline 2 \end{array}$$

8. R 143; 3
$$\begin{array}{r} \blacksquare\blacksquare\,R\,143;\,3 \\ 4\overline{)575} \\ -\,4 \\ \hline 17 \\ -\,16 \\ \hline 15 \\ -\,12 \\ \hline 3 \end{array}$$

9. $4\overline{)952}$
238

10. $3\overline{)761}$
253 R2

11. $5\overline{)615}$
123

12. $2\overline{)871}$
435 R1

13. $3\overline{)638}$
212 R2

E L L
STRATEGY
Visual
Learning

Visual Learning Animation

www.pearsonsuccessnet.com or CD

Why did you round 378 to 360 rather than to 380 or 400 in order to estimate? [Since I am dividing by 3, I chose the number that is compatible with 3.]

Divide the tens.

```
  12
3)378
 -3
  7
 -6
  1
```

After you divide the tens, are there any remaining? [Yes, there is 1 ten remaining.] *What do you do with the remaining ten?* [I trade it for 10 ones.] *How many ones are there now?* [18]

Divide the ones.

```
  126
3)378
 -3
  7
 -6
  18
 -18
  0
```

There are 126 watches in each box.

The answer is reasonable because 126 is close to 120.

Is the quotient reasonable? Explain. [Yes; the estimated quotient is 120, and 126 is close to 120.] *How can you check that the quotient is correct?* [Multiply 126 by 3.]

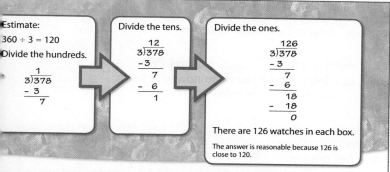

Estimate:
360 ÷ 3 = 120

Divide the hundreds.

```
  1
3)378
 -3
  7
```

Divide the tens.

```
  12
3)378
 -3
  7
 -6
  1
```

Divide the ones.

```
  126
3)378
 -3
  7
 -6
  18
 -18
  0
```

There are 126 watches in each box.

The answer is reasonable because 126 is close to 120.

Problem Solving **MATHEMATICAL PRACTICES**

14. Reason The largest United States flag ever created was displayed at the Hoover Dam. The flag measures 255 feet by 505 feet. How many feet longer is the flag than it is wide? **250 feet longer**

Width: 255 feet
Length: 505 feet

For **15** and **16**, use the table at the right.

15. There are 848 people getting on board the *Memphis Belle*. How many seats are needed for every person to sit? **212 seats**

16. Writing to Explain If 793 people are on the *Natchez Willie*, how many seats are needed for each person to sit? **133; 793 ÷ 6 = 132 R1; If each person is going to sit, another seat is needed.**

17. If 698 ÷ 4 = 174 R ▢, what is the value of ▢? **2**

18. The Galveston-Port Bolivar Ferry takes cars across Galveston Bay. One day, the ferry transported a total of 685 cars over a 5-hour period. If the ferry took the same number of cars each hour, how many cars did it take each hour? **137 cars**

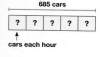
685 cars

| ? | ? | ? | ? | ? |

↑
cars each hour

Data	**Historic River Boat Tours**	
	Natchez Willie	6 riders per seat
	Memphis Belle	4 riders per seat

19. Persevere Theo bought a T-shirt for $21 and a pair of shorts for $16. He paid with two $20 bills. How much money did Theo get back?

A $1
B $2
C $3
D $4

Close

Essential Understanding The standard division algorithm breaks the calculation into simpler calculations using basic facts, place-value, the relationship between multiplication and division, and estimation.
In this lesson, you learned how to divide a 3-digit number by a 1-digit number.

 ASSESSMENT

Exercises 1 and 2 are worth 1 point each.
Use the rubric to score Exercise 3.

Exercise 3

Writing to Explain Students should be able to identify the importance of estimation and be able to show it.

ELL Provide Sentence Stems For students who need additional writing support, provide these sentence stems to help them structure their answers:

To find how many tables are at the diner, I need to _____ [divide] 786 by 5. The quotient will have a _____. [remainder] The remainder will tell me how many people are not _____ [sitting] at a table.

Student Samples
3-point answer The student divides correctly and also gives a logical explanation for his or her answer.

> I divided 786 by 5 to get 157 R1. There are 157 tables at the diner with 5 people sitting at each. The remainder, 1, means that there is one person who cannot sit at one of the tables.

2-point answer The student shows that he or she understands division with 3-digit numbers but does not explain his or her answer.

> $768 \div 5 = 157 \text{ R } 1$

1-point answer The student understands how to divide 3-digit numbers but does not come up with the correct answer.

> $$\begin{array}{r} 157 \\ 5\overline{)786} \\ \underline{5} \\ 28 \\ \underline{25} \\ 36 \\ -36 \end{array}$$

Quick Check Master

Name _____

Quick Check
10-5

1. In one week, the Evanston Recycling Center received 784 aluminum cans. They received the same number of cans each day. How many cans did the recycling center receive each day?
   (A) 112
   B 114
   C 121
   D 122

2. Zoe is helping her parents at their store, The Sock Stop. She is organizing 658 pairs of socks into display boxes. Each display box holds 4 pairs of socks. How many pairs of socks are left over?
   A 3
   (B) 2
   C 1
   D 0

3. **Writing to Explain** There are 786 people at Dorothy's Diner. Five people can sit at a table. How many tables are in Dorothy's Diner? How many people cannot sit at one of the tables? Explain.
   See students' samples to the right.
   _____

 **Formative** Assessment

Use the **Quick Check** to assess students' understanding.

Prescription for Differentiated Instruction
Use student work on the **Quick Check** to prescribe differentiated instruction.

Points	Prescription
0–2	Intervention
3–4	On-Level
5	Advanced

Differentiated Instruction

Intervention

Dividing 3-Digit by 1-Digit Numbers

 10–15 min

- Have students solve $7\overline{)859}$.

- Display the problem on the board. Using a sheet of paper, cover the 9 so only $7\overline{)85}$ is showing.

- Have students solve the problem $7\overline{)85}$ using prior knowledge. *What is the quotient of $7\overline{)85}$?* [12] *What is the remainder?* [1]

- Uncover the 9. *What is the value of the remainder?* [1 ten] *Regroup the 1 ten and 9 ones as 19 ones. Continue dividing.*

- *What is the new quotient?* [122] *What is the new remainder?* [5]

- Repeat for $7\overline{)519}$, which has a two-digit quotient. [74 R1]

On-Level

Practice — **Center Activity**

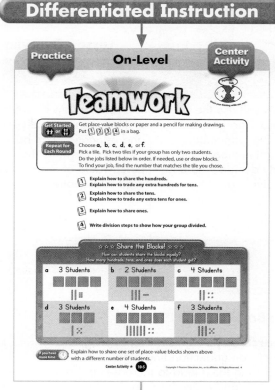

Advanced

Practice — **Center Activity**

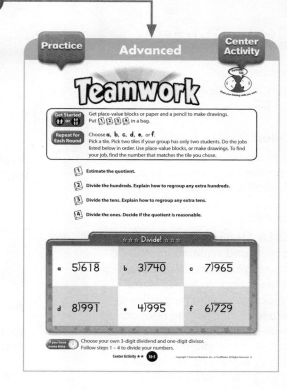

ELL Partner Talk Listen for language that describes sharing place-value blocks. For example, a student might say, "To start dividing 435 by 3, figure out how many hundreds each student can get."

Leveled Homework

Reteaching Master

Practice Master

Enrichment Master

Also available in print

Domain
Number and Operations in Base Ten

Cluster
Use place value understanding and properties of operations to perform multi-digit arithmetic.

Standard
4.NBT.6 Find whole-number quotients and remainders with up to four-digit dividends and one-digit divisors, using strategies based on place value, the properties of operations, and/or the relationship between multiplication and division. Illustrate and explain the calculation by using equations, rectangular arrays, and/or area models.

Mathematical Practices

✔ Make sense of problems and persevere in solving them.

✔ Reason abstractly and quantitatively.

✔ Construct viable arguments and critique the reasoning of others.

✔ Model with mathematics.

○ Use appropriate tools strategically.

○ Attend to precision.

○ Look for and make use of structure.

○ Look for and express regularity in repeated reasoning.

Deciding Where to Start Dividing

 **Lesson Overview**

Objective	Essential Understanding	Vocabulary	Materials
Students will use the standard algorithm to divide 3-digit numbers by 1-digit numbers and properly decide where to begin dividing.	The relationship between multiplication and division and estimation can be used to determine the place value of the largest digit in a quotient.		Place-value blocks (Teaching Tool 8) (*2 hundreds, 20 tens, and 40 ones per pair*)

PROFESSIONAL DEVELOPMENT

Math Background

Research says ... instructional programs that focus on understanding algorithms before using them lead to increases in both conceptual and procedural knowledge (Mathematical Learning Study Committee, 2001). In this lesson, students decide where to begin dividing a 3-digit dividend. In previous lessons students have studied and mastered the algorithm for division. Students can now apply this algorithm.

When dividing the example across the top of pages 242–243, students should be able to picture the 1 hundreds flat, 4 tens rods, and 5 unit cubes as they begin their division. Using the previous algorithm, they should begin dividing the hundreds place. Since there is only 1 hundred, students must regroup the hundred as 10 tens and then continue to divide. Based upon their understanding, it should make sense to students that the first digit of the quotient, or 3, belongs in the tens place, since there were 3 tens placed in each group.

1 Daily Common Core Review

Daily Common Core Review

Name _____

Daily Common Core Review
10-6

1. **Mental Math** Joe is the 56th person in line for concert tickets. His friend Mary is 2 places behind him. What is Mary's place in line?
   A 54th
   B 57th
   C 58th
   D 59th

2. Helen and Grace are working on a geography project together. They must find the state capitals for each of the 50 states. They decide that they will each research the same number of states. How many capitals will each girl find?
   A 2
   B 10
   C 25
   D 50

3. Every year, Kevin's grandmother sends him $20 for his birthday. Kevin always saves his birthday money. He is now 9 years old. How much money has he saved?
   A $200
   B $180
   C $170
   D $100

4. Jorge has $17. He wants to buy two books. One costs $5. The other costs $12. Does he have enough money?
   Yes

5. Margo, Linda, and Liz are sisters. Margo is 8. Linda is twice as old as Margo. Liz is 4 years younger than Linda. How much older than Margo is Liz?
   4 years

Also available in print

Content Reviewed

Exercise 1   Problem Solving

Exercise 2   Division

Exercise 3   Multiplication

Exercise 4   Multi-Step Problems

Exercise 5   Problem Solving

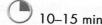

 10–15 min # Problem-Based Interactive Learning

Overview Students will use place-value blocks to model division when the quotient has fewer digits than the dividend.

Focus What do you do when there are not enough hundreds to divide?

Materials Place-value blocks or Teaching Tool 8 (*2 hundreds, 20 tens, and 40 ones per pair*)

Set the Purpose *You have learned to divide 3-digit numbers. Today, you will be learning what to do when there are not enough hundreds to divide.*

Connect Tell students that division is used everyday. *If you want to share a package of 100 paper plates among 3 classes, you'll have to divide even though there are not enough hundreds to share equally.*

MATHEMATICAL PRACTICES

Model with Mathematics
When students use place-value blocks to decide where to start dividing, they are modeling with mathematics.

Pose the Problem *Roberto is using craft sticks to make picture frames. He has 152 craft sticks. He uses 6 sticks for each frame. How many frames can he make?* Distribute place-value blocks to students. Allow students to work in pairs to solve this problem, using place-value blocks as models. Then have them share their work with the class.

Instruct in Small Steps Once students have found and discussed their own solutions, work through the problem as a class. *What division problem can you use to answer the question?* [152 ÷ 6] *First divide the hundreds. How many hundreds can you put in each group?* [0] *Why?* [There are not enough hundreds to put 1 in each of 6 groups.] *How many tens make up 1 hundred?* [10]. *How many tens do you have in all?* [15] *How many tens go in each group?* [2] *Are there any tens remaining?* [3 tens remain.] *Now what?* [Trade the 3 tens for 30 ones.] *How many ones do you have in all?* [32] *How many ones go in each group? Are there any ones remaining?* [5 ones; 2 ones remain] *Does Roberto have enough craft sticks to make 28 frames? Explain.* [No; 152 ÷ 6 = 25 R2, so Roberto can only make 25 frames. He will have 2 craft sticks left over.] Ask students to record their work. Offer assistance to students having difficulty writing the algorithm.

Small-Group Interaction On the board, write 3)459 and 5)459. *Work with your partner. Decide where you would start to divide to find each quotient. Explain your decision for the first problem to your partner. Have your partner explain his or her decision for the second problem to you.*

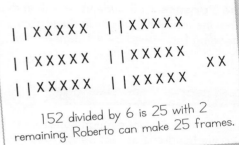

I I X X X X X   I I X X X X X
I I X X X X X   I I X X X X X   X X
I I X X X X X   I I X X X X X

152 divided by 6 is 25 with 2 remaining. Roberto can make 25 frames.

$$\begin{array}{r} 25\ R2 \\ 6\overline{)152} \\ -12 \\ \hline 32 \\ -30 \\ \hline 2 \end{array}$$

Roberto has enough craft sticks to make 25 frames.

Use the digits 2, 3, 4, and 5 to write a division problem that will have a 3-digit quotient and a problem that will have a 2-digit quotient. [Possible answers: 345 ÷ 2; 234 ÷ 5]

eTools **Place-Value Blocks**
www.pearsonsuccessnet.com

Visual Learning

Deciding Where to Start Dividing

What do you do when there aren't enough hundreds to divide?

Madison is making iguana key chains using pom-poms. She has 145 pink pom-poms. Are there enough pink pom-poms to make 36 key chains?

4 pink pom-poms

2 yellow pom-poms
4 pink pom-poms
7 blue pom-poms
31 green pom-poms
3 yards of plastic lace

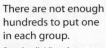

How many pink pom-poms does Madison have? [145] *How many pink pom-poms does she need for each key chain?* [4] *What division problem must you complete to solve the problem?* [145 divided by 4]

There are not enough hundreds to put one in each group.

Start by dividing the tens.

$$
\begin{array}{r}
3 \\
4\overline{)145} \\
-12 \\
\hline
2\,5
\end{array}
$$

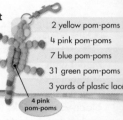

Prevent Misconceptions

Some students may write the quotient in the hundreds place even if they start by dividing tens. Suggest that they make an X in the hundreds place of the quotient as soon as they decide that there are not enough hundreds to divide.

---

1 Visual Learning

Set the Purpose Call students' attention to the **Visual Learning Bridge** at the top of the page. *In the lesson, you will learn where to start dividing a dividend by a 1-digit divisor.*

2 Guided Practice

 MATHEMATICAL PRACTICES

Sometimes there are not enough hundreds to divide. Students must regroup the hundreds as tens before they can begin dividing.

Exercise 3
Error Intervention

If students are having difficulty deciding where to start dividing,

then ask: *If you have 3 flats, can you divide them into 7 equal groups?* [No] *If you have 36 tens rods, can you divide them into 7 equal groups?* [Yes] *How many rods are in each group?* [5]

Reteaching Model where to start dividing a 3-digit number by a 1-digit divisor, such as 755 ÷ 9. For another example and more practice, assign **Reteaching** Set F on p. 250.

3 Independent Practice

Remind students to use estimation to help decide what the quotient will look like. Use Exercise 10 as an example. *Use 700 ÷ 5 to estimate. The estimated quotient is 140; therefore the exact answer will have 3 digits.*

Lesson 10-6

Common Core

4.NBT.6 Find whole-number quotients and remainders with up to four-digit dividends and one-digit divisors, using strategies based on place value, the properties of operations, and/or the relationship between multiplication and division. Illustrate and explain the calculation by using equations, rectangular arrays, and/or area models.

Deciding Where to Start Dividing

What do you do when there aren't enough hundreds to divide?

Madison is making iguana key chains using pom-poms. She has 145 pink pom-poms. Are there enough pink pom-poms to make 36 key chains?

4 pink pom-poms

2 yellow pom-poms
4 pink pom-poms
7 blue pom-poms
31 green pom-poms
3 yards of plastic lace

MATHEMATICAL PRACTICES

Guided Practice*

Do you know HOW?

In **1** and **2**, copy and complete each calculation.

1.
$$
\begin{array}{r}
6\;5 \\
7\overline{)455} \\
-\;42 \\
\hline
5\,3 \\
-\;35 \\
\hline
0
\end{array}
$$

2.
$$
\begin{array}{r}
\blacksquare\,\blacksquare\; R\;63;\,4 \\
5\overline{)319} \\
-3 \\
\hline
\blacksquare\,9 \\
-\blacksquare15 \\
\hline
4
\end{array}
$$

Do you UNDERSTAND?

3. Madison has 365 blue pom-poms. How many key chains can she make 52 key chains

4. **Communicate** Explain how an estimated quotient can help you decide where to start. If the esti quotient is greater than 100, st dividing the hundreds. If it is les 100, divide the tens.

Independent Practice

Leveled Practice In **5** through **13**, divide. You may draw a picture to help you.

5.
$$
\begin{array}{r}
\blacksquare\,74 \\
6\overline{)444} \\
-\blacksquare\;42 \\
\hline
24 \\
-\blacksquare\;24 \\
\hline
0
\end{array}
$$

6.
$$
\begin{array}{r}
1\,\blacksquare\,96 \\
3\overline{)588} \\
-\blacksquare\;3 \\
\hline
8\;2 \\
-\blacksquare\;27 \\
\hline
8\,1 \\
-\blacksquare18 \\
\hline
0
\end{array}
$$

7.
$$
\begin{array}{r}
5\,\blacksquare\; R\,2;\,1 \\
8\overline{)417} \\
-\blacksquare\;40 \\
\hline
17 \\
-\blacksquare\;16 \\
\hline
1
\end{array}
$$

8.
$$
\begin{array}{r}
\blacksquare\,\blacksquare\; R\;467;\,1 \\
2\overline{)935} \\
-8 \\
\hline
13 \\
-\blacksquare12 \\
\hline
15 \\
-\blacksquare14 \\
\hline
1
\end{array}
$$

9. $8\overline{)526}$
65 R6

10. $5\overline{)690}$
138

11. $3\overline{)769}$
256 R1

12. $4\overline{)923}$
230 R3

13. $6\overline{)342}$
57

Divide the ones.

$$\begin{array}{r} 36\text{R}1 \\ 4\overline{)145} \\ -\ 12 \\ \hline 25 \\ -\ 24 \\ \hline 1 \end{array}$$

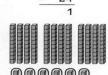

How many ones are being divided? [25] *What can you tell from the quotient and the remainder?* [Madison can make 36 key chains, with one pom-pom left over.]

To check, multiply the quotient by the divisor and add the remainder.

$$\begin{array}{r} 2 \\ 36 \\ \times\ 4 \\ \hline 144 \end{array}$$

144 + 1 = 145

Madison has enough pink pom-poms to make 36 key chains.

Why do you add the remainder to check the division? [I subtracted to find the remainder. Since addition is the inverse of subtraction, I can use it to check my work.]

There are not enough hundreds to put one in each group.

start by dividing the tens.

$$\begin{array}{r} 3 \\ 4\overline{)145} \\ -\ 12 \\ \hline 25 \end{array}$$

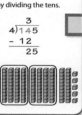

Divide the ones.

$$\begin{array}{r} 36\ \text{R}1 \\ 4\overline{)145} \\ -\ 12 \\ \hline 25 \\ -\ 24 \\ \hline 1 \end{array}$$

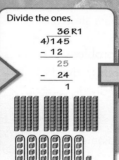

To check, multiply the quotient by the divisor and add the remainder.

$$\begin{array}{r} 2 \\ 36 \\ \times\ 4 \\ \hline 144 \end{array}$$

144 + 1 = 145

Madison has enough pink pom-poms to make 36 key chains.

n 14 through 23, divide. Then check your answer.

4. 6)96 **16**	15. 5)295 **59**	16. 2)306 **153**	17. 9)517 **57 R4**	18. 4)624 **156**
9. 7)430 **61 R3**	20. 4)229 **57 R1**	21. 5)655 **131**	22. 3)209 **69 R2**	23. 6)438 **73**

Problem Solving | **MATHEMATICAL PRACTICES**

or 24 and 25, use the bar graph at the right.

ames is organizing his CDs. He plans to put hem into stackable cubes that hold 8 CDs each.

4. How many cubes will James need for his entire collection?
32 cubes

5. If James decides to group his Rock and World music CDs together, how many cubes would he need for them?
23 cubes

6. **Reason** How can you tell without dividing that 479 ÷ 6 will have a 2-digit quotient? **6 is greater than 4, so you need to start dividing at the tens.**

7. **Persevere** A family is going on a trip for 3 days. The total cost for the hotel is $336. They budgeted $100 a day for food. How much will each day of the trip cost?

A $33 B $112 C $145 **D** $212

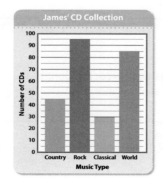

James' CD Collection

Number of CDs / Country Rock Classical World / Music Type

Lesson 10-6 **243**

Problem Solving | **MATHEMATICAL PRACTICES**

Students use underlying processes and mathematical tools for Exercises 24–27. Remind students to use estimation to check for reasonableness when solving each problem.

Exercise 27

Make Sense of Problems Remind students to read the problem carefully and pick out the important words that will help them solve the problem. *Is $336 the cost of the hotel for three days or for one day? How do you know?* [3 days; the problem says "total cost."] *Is $100 the cost of the food for three days or for one day? How do you know?* [1 day; the problem says "a day."] *How do you find the cost for 1 day?* [Divide 336 by 3 and add 100.]

Early Finishers In Exercises 24 and 25, if James decides to put his Country and Classical CDs together, how many cubes would he need? [He will need 10 cubes. Nine cubes will be full, and the tenth cube will have 3 CDs.]

Close

Essential Understanding The relationship between multiplication and division and estimation can be used to determine the place value of the largest digit in a quotient. *In this lesson, you learned how to decide where to start dividing a 3-digit number by a 1-digit number.*

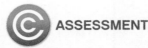 **ASSESSMENT**

Exercises 1 and 2 are worth 1 point each.
Use the rubric to score Exercise 3.

Exercise 3

Writing to Explain Students correctly determine which problems will have 3-digit quotients. Students provide a logical explanation for their reasoning.

ELL Suggest a Sequence For students who need additional writing support, provide the following sequence to help them structure their answers:

First, I will look at how many hundreds there are in each problem.

Then, I will cross out the problems without enough hundreds to divide.

Finally, I will select the problems with enough hundreds to divide.

Student Samples
3-point answer The student correctly identifies the problems that have 3-digit quotients. The student provides a logical explanation of his or her reasoning.

> I looked at the hundreds place in each dividend. Problems a, c, and d had enough hundreds to divide into at least once with the divisor, so I knew I could divide to get 3-digit quotients.

2-point answer The student correctly identifies at least one of the problems that have 3-digit quotients but also identifies wrong answers. The student does not provide a clear explanation of his or her reasoning.

> Problems a, b, and e will have 3-digit quotients. I knew I could divide to get 3-digit quotients.

1-point answer The student does not correctly identify the problems and does not provide an explanation of his or her reasoning.

> Problems b and f.

Quick Check Master

Name _____

Quick Check
10-6

1. Lucy has a card-making business. She has an order to make 65 cards in 8 days. She makes the same number of cards each day for 7 days. How many cards does she have to make on the 8th day?

   A 0
   B 1
   C 2
   D 3

2. A shipment of 8 boxes just arrived at Litman's Bookstore. Each box holds the same number of books. If there are 744 books in the shipment, how many books are in each box?

   A 193
   B 103
   C 93
   D 90

3. **Writing to Explain** Which of the following problems will have 3-digit quotients? How do you know?

   a. 2⟌621   b. 3⟌152   c. 4⟌912

   d. 5⟌734   e. 6⟌452   f. 6⟌529

   See students' samples to the right.

 **Formative** Assessment

Use the **Quick Check** to assess students' understanding.

Prescription for Differentiated Instruction
Use student work on the **Quick Check** to prescribe differentiated instruction.

Points	Prescription
0–2	Intervention
3–4	On-Level
5	Advanced

Differentiated Instruction

Intervention

Deciding Where to Start Dividing

 10–15 min or

Materials Centimeter grid paper (Teaching Tool 4)

- Have students write $5\overline{)259}$, putting one digit in each square.

- *Are there enough hundreds to put one into each of 5 groups?* [No] *How can you regroup the 2 hundreds and 5 tens as tens?* [25 tens]

- *How many tens are in each group?* [5] *How many tens are left?* [0 tens] *How many ones are in each group?* [1] *What is the quotient?* [51] *What is the remainder?* [4]

- Repeat for $4\overline{)347}$. [86 R3]

On-Level

Practice · **Center Activity**

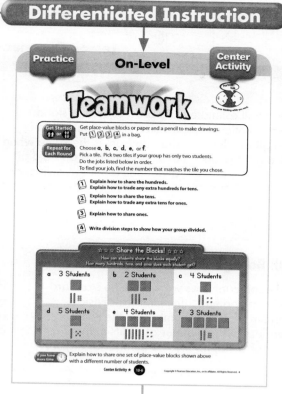

Advanced

Practice · **Center Activity**

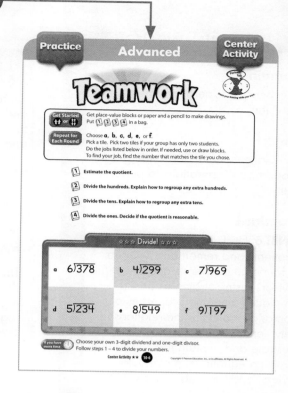

ELL Partner Talk Listen for explanations of where to start dividing. For example, a student might say, "If 4 students want to share 124 blocks, there aren't enough hundreds to share. Let's trade the hundred for tens."

Leveled Homework

Reteaching Master

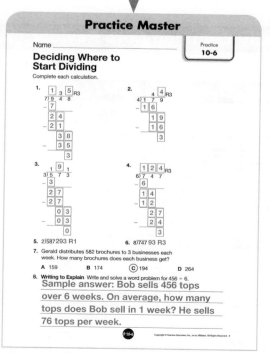

Also available in print

Practice Master

Also available in print

Enrichment Master

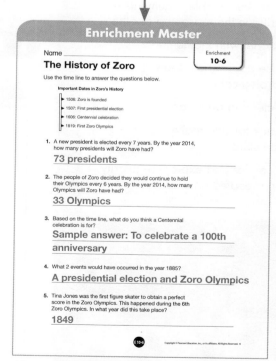

Also available in print

Common Core

Domain
Number and Operations in Base Ten

Cluster
Use place value understanding and properties of operations to perform multi-digit arithmetic.

Standard
4.NBT.6 Find whole-number quotients and remainders with up to four-digit dividends and one-digit divisors, using strategies based on place value, the properties of operations, and/or the relationship between multiplication and division. Illustrate and explain the calculation by using equations, rectangular arrays, and/or area models.

Mathematical Practices
○ Make sense of problems and persevere in solving them.

✔ Reason abstractly and quantitatively.

✔ Construct viable arguments and critique the reasoning of others.

○ Model with mathematics.

○ Use appropriate tools strategically.

○ Attend to precision.

○ Look for and make use of structure.

✔ Look for and express regularity in repeated reasoning.

Dividing 4-Digit by 1-Digit Numbers

 **Lesson Overview**

Objective	Essential Understanding	Vocabulary	Materials
Students will estimate and find quotients for 4-digit dividends and 1-digit divisors.	The process for the standard division algorithm with one-digit divisors is the same when extended from 2- and 3-digit dividends to 4-digit dividends.		

 PROFESSIONAL DEVELOPMENT

Math Background

This lesson continues work with the standard division algorithm. The standard division algorithm for whole numbers is the same regardless of the number of digits in the divisor or dividend. As the number of digits in the dividend and/or divisor increases, estimating quotients becomes particularly important for checking the reasonableness of the quotient.

1 Daily Common Core Review

Daily Common Core Review

Name _____

Daily Common Core Review **10-7**

1. **Mental Math** Elizabeth is baking cookies. She has invited 6 people to her house. She wants each guest to have 4 cookies. How many cookies does she need to bake for her guests?

A 20
B 22
Ⓒ 24
D 26

2. **Mental Math** There were 32 students going on a field trip. Each van could carry 8 students. Which number sentence is in the same fact family as 32 ÷ 8 = ☐?

Ⓐ 4 × ☐ = 32
B 32 × 8 = ☐
C ☐ × 4 = 8
D 8 × 8 = ☐

3. **Mental Math** In which of the following does 5 make the number sentence true?

A 3 × 2 = ☐
B ☐ × 6 = 42
Ⓒ 9 × ☐ = 45
D ☐ × 3 = 18

4. Jacob's rock collection is shown below. What fraction of his rocks is gray?

A $\frac{1}{4}$
B $\frac{1}{3}$
Ⓒ $\frac{3}{4}$
D $\frac{4}{3}$

5. Arthur, Jorge, and Dylan collected a total of 328 cans to recycle. Arthur collected 105 and Jorge collected 112. How many cans did Dylan collect?

111 cans

6. **Mental Math** Complete the fact family below. Explain what the fact family shows.

The fact family shows all the related multiplication and division facts for 6, 7, and 42.

7 × 6 = 42
6 × 7 = 42
42 ÷ 7 = **6**
42 ÷ 6 = 7

Also available in print

Content Reviewed
Exercise 1 Multiplication

Exercise 2 Fact Families

Exercise 3 Multiplication Facts

Exercise 4 Fraction of a Set

Exercise 5 Addition and Subtraction

Exercise 6 Fact Families

 10–15 min # Problem-Based Interactive Learning

Overview Students will estimate quotients for 4-digit dividends and 1-digit divisors.

Focus How can you estimate larger quotients?

Set the Purpose *You have learned how to find exact quotients for whole-number dividends. Today you will learn how to estimate and find quotients for division with 4-digit dividends and 1-digit divisors.* Have students work in pairs and share their solution strategies.

Connect *Have you ever had a situation where you had to decide if information was reasonable?* [Possible answer: Deciding how much time is needed to complete homework; deciding how long it takes to travel somewhere.]

MATHEMATICAL
PRACTICES

Make Generalizations
Students should use estimation to make generalizations about the quotients of division problems.

Pose the Problem *A high school football stadium has 6 sections that each seat the same number of people. A total of 1,950 people can be seated in the stadium. About how many people can be seated in each section? (a) Use estimation to give two multiples of 100 between which the exact quotient falls. (b) Then give a single number as an estimate of the quotient.*

Use Prior Knowledge *In previous lessons you have estimated quotients and found exact quotients for whole-number dividends up to 3 digits and 1-digit divisors.*

Instruct in Small Steps Emphasize the relationship between multiplication and division together with basic division facts and place value to estimate quotients. *Is 1,950 ÷ 6 more than 10?* [Yes] *More than 100?* [Yes.] *More than 1,000? Explain.* [No. 6 × 1,000 = 6,000 which is greater than 1,950.] *What basic facts can be used to estimate 1,950 ÷ 6?* [18 ÷ 6 = 3 and 24 ÷ 6 = 4.] *Between which multiples of 100 does the exact quotient fall? How do you know?* [6 × 300 = 1,800 and 6 × 400 = 2,400. Since 1,950 is between 1,800 and 2,400 the exact quotient is between 300 and 400.]

Is the exact quotient closer to 300 or 400? How do you know? [300; 1,950 is closer to 1,800 than to 2,400.] *What is a reasonable estimate for 1,950 ÷ 6?* [A little less than 350 because 2,100 is halfway between 1,800 and 2,400 and 350 is halfway between 300 and 400.]

Choose two different numbers for x so (x ÷ 5) is between 250 and 300. Tell how you decided. [Sample answer: 5 × 300 = 1,500 and 5 × 200 = 1,000 so x can be any number that is less than but close to 1,500.]

Visual Learning

Dividing 4-Digit by 1-Digit Numbers

How can you estimate larger quotients?

In all, 4,729 hot dogs were sold at a football game. If there are 8 hot dogs in a package, how many packages of hot dogs were sold?

4,729 hot dogs sold

4,729 hot dogs in all

? packages

8

Hot dogs in each package

Why is this a division situation? [Finding how many 8s are in 4,729 can be modeled using division.]

Estimate. Decide where to start.

$500 \times 8 = 4,000$
The answer is more than 500.

$600 \times 8 = 4,800$
The answer is less than but close to 600.

Start dividing in the hundreds.

---

1 Visual Learning

Set the Purpose Call students' attention to the **Visual Learning Bridge** at the top of the page. *In this lesson you will practice dividing three-digit and four-digit numbers by one-digit numbers and learn to use estimation to check the reasonableness of the quotients.*

2 Guided Practice — MATHEMATICAL PRACTICES

Exercise 4
Remind students to estimate quotients first. Point out that when a quotient involves a remainder, they only need to compare the quotient, not the quotient and remainder, to the estimate.

Error Intervention

If students are having difficulty determining if a quotient is reasonable,

then guide them to understand that the quotient must be close to the estimate. *Suppose you and two friends were equally dividing money you earned working together. You estimated that each person's share would be $85. Would you think it was reasonable if you were given $48?* [No] *What exact amounts would you consider reasonable?* [Answers will vary but should be in the range of $80 to $90.]

Reteaching Ask students to explain how they would check the reasonableness of the actual quotient for $323 \div 5$. [Before dividing, I would use compatible numbers to estimate the quotient: $300 \div 5 = 60$. After dividing, I would check if my actual quotient is close to 60.] For another example and more practice, assign **Reteaching** Set G on p. 251.

3 Independent Practice

Remind students to estimate first and then use their estimates twice. Use Exercise 9 as an example. *Using compatible numbers, what is your estimate?* [$1,200 \div 6 = 200$] *In what two ways will you use your estimate?* [To determine that I should place the first digit of the quotient in the hundreds place and to check if my quotient is reasonable when I finish dividing.]

Lesson 10-7

Common Core

4.NBT.6 Find whole-number quotients and remainders with up to four-digit dividends and one-digit divisors, using strategies based on place value, the properties of operations, and/or the relationship between multiplication and division. Illustrate and explain the calculation by using equations, rectangular arrays, and/or area models.

Dividing 4-Digit by 1-Digit Numbers

How can you estimate larger quotients?

In all, 4,729 hot dogs were sold at a football game. If there are 8 hot dogs in a package, how many packages of hot dogs were sold?

4,729 hot dogs sold

4,729 hot dogs in all

? packages

8

Hot dogs in each package

Guided Practice* — MATHEMATICAL PRACTICES

Do you know HOW?
Divide. Start by estimating.
Estimates will vary.

1. $9)\overline{2,871}$ 319

2. $4)\overline{2,486}$ 621 R2

3. $9)\overline{691}$ 76 R7

4. $4)\overline{1,140}$ 285

Do you UNDERSTAND?

5. **Reason** In the example above, how many hot dogs were left over in the extra package?
$8 - 1 = 7$ hot dogs

6. **Writing to Explain** Vickie's estimated quotient was 80. The actual quotient she calculated was 48. Is her actual quotient reasonable? Explain. See margin.

Independent Practice

Divide. Start by estimating. **Estimates will vary.**

7. $8)\overline{3,248}$ 406

8. $5)\overline{247}$ 49 R2

9. $6)\overline{1,380}$ 230

10. $5)\overline{3,980}$ 796

In **11** through **16**, estimate first. Tell if the answers are reasonable. If the answer is not reasonable, find the correct answer.

11. $\overset{61\ R1}{6)\overline{367}}$ Yes

12. $3)\overline{3,582}$ No; 1,194 (911 R6)

13. $\overset{49\ R2}{5)\overline{247}}$ Yes

14. $9)\overline{1,745}$ No; 193 R8 (93 R8)

15. $\overset{53\ R4}{7)\overline{375}}$ Yes

16. $8)\overline{1,535}$ No; 191 R7 (91 R7)

 244 *For another example, see Set G on page 251.*

---

6. Sample answer: No; The numbers are not very close, so her answer is not reasonable. Either her actual quotient or her estimate is incorrect.

Which basic division facts help you estimate? [$40 \div 8 = 5$ and $48 \div 8 = 6$] *How do you know the answer is close to 600?* [4,729 is closer to 4,800 than 4,000, so the answer is closer to 600 than 500.]

Divide.

```
        591 R1
    8)4,729          47 hundreds ÷ 8 is about 5 hundreds
     -40             8 × 5 = 40
      72             72 tens ÷ 8 is 9 tens
     - 72            8 × 9 = 72
       09            9 ones ÷ 8 is about 1 one
      -  8           8 × 1 = 8
         1
```

591 complete packages were sold and 1 hot dog was sold from another package.

How can you check your work? [$591 \times 8 = 4,728$; $4,728 + 1 = 4,729$] *Does the answer seem reasonable? Explain.* [Yes. The estimate and the exact answer are close to each other.]

Estimate. Decide where to start.

$500 \times 8 = 4,000$
The answer is more than 500.

$600 \times 8 = 4,800$
The answer is less than but close to 600.

Start dividing in the hundreds.

Divide.

```
        591 R1
    8)4,729          47 hundreds ÷ 8 is about 5 hundreds
     -40             8 × 5 = 40
      72             72 tens ÷ 8 is 9 tens
     - 72            8 × 9 = 72
       09            9 ones ÷ 8 is about 1 one
      -  8           8 × 1 = 8
         1
```

591 complete packages were sold and 1 hot dog was sold from another package.

Problem Solving
MATHEMATICAL PRACTICES

Solve. Record your work.

17. A family of four drove from San Francisco to New York. They drove the same number of miles each day for 6 days. How many miles did they drive each day? What does the remainder mean? 484 R2; The family has 2 miles to go after driving 484 miles for 6 days.

2,906 miles
San Francisco — New York

18. **Reason** Without dividing, how can you tell that the quotient for $5,873 \div 8$ is greater than 700? Is the quotient less than 800? Explain. See margin.

19. **Reason** Chose a value for x so that $x \div 5$ is between 400 and 500. Tell how you decided. See margin.

20. **Music** A square dance set is made up of 4 couples (8 dancers). Each couple stands on one of the four sides of a square. There are 150 people at a square dance. What is the greatest number of sets possible at the dance?

Ⓐ 18   **B** 19   **C** 37   **D** 38

21. Michelle traveled 498 miles from Lakeside to West Little River. She made 7 stops at equal intervals, including her final stop. Michelle estimated that she drove about 50 miles between stops. Is her estimate reasonable? Explain. See margin.

22. Mr. Girard sells fishing supplies. He traveled 527 miles from Jacksonville to Miami. He made 6 stops at equal intervals, including his final stop. About how many miles did he travel between stops? About 90

23. Alycia has 164 treats to give to the 7 goats at the petting zoo. Each goat gets an equal share of the treats. How many treats will each goat get? How many treats will Alycia have left? 23; 3

Lesson 10-7   245

Problem Solving
MATHEMATICAL PRACTICES

Students use underlying processes and mathematical tools for Exercises 17–23. Remind students to use estimation to check for reasonableness when solving each problem.

Exercise 19

Reason Abstractly If students need help with this problem, discuss the steps to take to solve it. *The value of x divided by 5 must be between 400 and 500. How can you find the value of x?* [Multiply 5 by 400 and 500.] *What is 5×400?* [2,000] *What is 5×500?* [2,500] *What value of x divided by 5 will give a quotient between 400 and 500?* [Any number between 2,000 and 2,500]

Exercise 20

Test-Taking Tip: Make Smart Choices Remind students that they can often eliminate wrong answers and work backward from a given answer. *How many dancers make up one set?* [8] *How can you use estimation to eliminate some wrong answers?* [$160 \div 8 = 20$, so Choices C and D are not reasonable answers.] *How can you work backward to find whether Choice A or Choice B is correct?* [Multiply each number by 8 to find which choice gives the greater number less than or equal to 150.]

Early Finishers Have student pairs play this game using a set of number cards from 0–9 placed face down. Partner 1 writes a two-digit multiple of 10. Partner 2 draws four cards. Both players arrange the four digits to write a problem for a three-digit number divided by a one-digit number. The player whose quotient is closer to the multiple of 10 earns 1 point. Trade roles. The first player to earn 3 points wins.

Journal Ask students to explain how they can use estimation to check the reasonableness of a quotient.

18. Sample answer: $8 \times 700 = 5,600$, which is less than 5,873. 8×800 is 6,400, which is more than 5,873. The quotient must be between 700 and 800.

19. Sample answer: 2,150; $5 \times 400 = 2,000$, and $5 \times 500 = 2,500$. I chose a number for x that was between 2,000 and 2,500.

21. No; $490 \div 7 = 70$, so she drove about 70 miles between stops.

Close

Essential Understanding The process for the standard division algorithm with one-digit divisors is the same when extended from 2- and 3-digit dividends to 4-digit dividends. *In this lesson, you learned to use estimation to decide if a quotient is reasonable.*

 ASSESSMENT

Exercises 1 and 2 are worth 1 point each.
Use the rubric to score Exercise 3.

Exercise 3

Writing to Explain Students estimate and find an exact quotient for a 4-digit number divided by a 1-digit number. They use the estimate to justify that the quotient is reasonable.

ELL Provide a Word List For students who need additional writing support, provide a list of words to use: *actual quotient, compatible numbers, close, estimate, reasonable.*

Student Samples
3-point answer The student estimates the quotient, and finds the actual quotient, using the estimate to check that it is reasonable.

2-point answer The student estimates the quotient and finds an actual quotient but does not fully explain how the estimate is used to check that the actual quotient is reasonable.

1-point answer The student incorrectly estimates the quotient and may or may not find the actual quotient. The student does not mention comparing the estimate to the quotient.

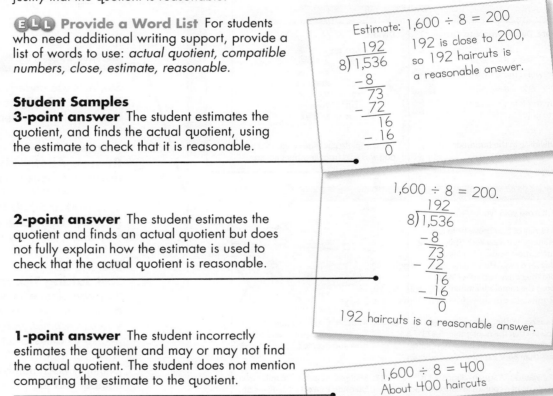

Quick Check Master

Name _____   Quick Check 10-7

Estimate. Then find each quotient. Use your estimate to check if your answer is reasonable.

1. Sam's father has an orchard of grapefruit trees. He has 3,429 trees that are arranged in 9 equal rows. What is 3,429 ÷ 9?

   A 340
   B 381
   C 400
   D 441

2. Ron's Tire Corral has 1,767 tires for heavy-duty trucks. Each heavy-duty truck needs 6 tires. How many trucks could get all new tires at Ron's, and how many tires would be left?

   A 280 trucks, 5 tires left
   B 291 trucks, 0 tires left
   C 294 trucks, 3 tires left
   D 300 trucks, 1 tire left

3. **Writing to Explain** Explain how you would estimate the answer to the problem shown below. Then check to see if your estimate is close to the actual quotient.

   In 8 days, a hair salon gave 1,536 haircuts. The salon gave the same number of haircuts each day. How many haircuts did the hair salon give each day?

   See students' samples at the right.

 **Formative** Assessment

Use the **Quick Check** to assess students' understanding.

Prescription for Differentiated Instruction
Use student work on the **Quick Check** to prescribe differentiated instruction.

Points	Prescription
0–2	**Intervention**
3–4	**On-Level**
5	**Advanced**

Differentiated Instruction

Intervention

 Dividing 4-Digit by 1-Digit Numbers

 10–15 min

- Have pairs of students fold a sheet of paper to make 3 rows of 3 boxes each. Ask them to write multiples of 10 from 10 to 90 in random order in the boxes to form a game board.

- Call out division problems. Pairs should use compatible numbers to estimate each quotient. Mark each estimate. The first pair to mark three estimates across, down, or diagonally wins.

- Call out the following problems in random order. 112 ÷ 9 [10], 135 ÷ 7 [20], 194 ÷ 6 [30], 305 ÷ 8 [40], 164 ÷ 3 [50], 516 ÷ 9 [60], 291 ÷ 4 [70], 153 ÷ 2 [80], 672 ÷ 7 [90].

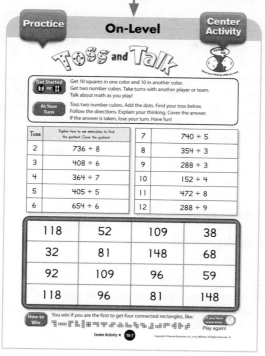

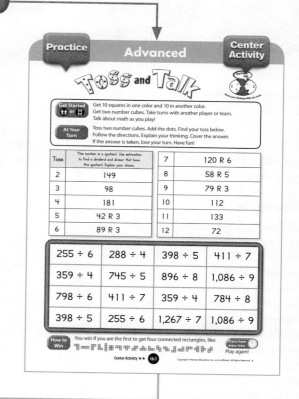

ELL Partner Talk Listen for evidence that a student is using estimation to check the reasonableness of the quotient. For example, a student might say, "If the quotient is 96, the dividend must be almost 100 times the divisor."

Leveled Homework

Reteaching Master

 Name _____ Reteaching 10-7

Dividing 4-Digit by 1-Digit Numbers

An estimate will help you decide where to place the first digit of the quotient. It will also help you check your answer.

Divide 5,493 ÷ 6.

Estimate first. You can use compatible numbers to divide mentally.

54 is a multiple of 6.

5,400 is close to 5,493 and 5,400 ÷ 6 will be easy to divide.

5,400 ÷ 6 = **900**

Divide to find the actual quotient.

    915 R3
6)5,493
  -54
    09
    -6
     33
    -30
      3

Compare: is the estimate close to the quotient?

estimate: **900**

quotient: **915 R3**

If it is, then your answer is reasonable.

Estimate. Then find each quotient. Use your estimate to check if your quotient is reasonable. **Sample estimates are given.**

1. Divide 4,318 ÷ 7.
   Estimate:
   4,200 ÷ **7** = **600**
   4,318 ÷ 7 = **616 R6**
   Is your answer reasonable? **Yes**

2. Divide 4,826 ÷ 5.
   Estimate:
   5,000 ÷ **5** = **1,000**
   4,826 ÷ 5 = **965 R1**
   Is your answer reasonable? **Yes**

3. Divide 4,377 ÷ 8.
   Estimate:
   4,000 ÷ **8** = **500**
   4,377 ÷ 8 = **547 R1**
   Is your answer reasonable? **Yes**

4. Divide 7,192 ÷ 9.
   Estimate:
   7,200 ÷ **9** = **800**
   7,192 ÷ 9 = **799 R1**
   Is your answer reasonable? **Yes**

Also available in print

Practice Master

Name _____ Practice 10-7

Dividing 4-Digit by 1-Digit Numbers

Estimate. Then find each quotient. Use your estimate to check if your answer is reasonable.

1. 4)1,227 **306 R3**   2. 5)2,438 **487 R3**   3. 8)4,904 **613**
4. 7)2,611 **373**   5. 6)4,998 **833**   6. 9)3,834 **426**
7. 3)1,675 **558 R1**   8. 4)1,254 **313 R2**
9. 544 ÷ 8 = **68**   10. 2,430 ÷ 6 = **405**

11. At the airport, there are 1,160 seats in the waiting areas. There are 8 separate, same size, waiting areas. How many seats are in each waiting area? **145 seats**

12. A wall by the school parking lot has an area of 1,666 square feet. Seven teams of students will paint a mural on the wall. Each team will paint an equal area of the wall. How many square feet will each team paint? **238 square feet**

13. **Geometry** Conner put a fence around the perimeter of his rectangular yard. The perimeter of the yard is 858 feet. Conner put a fence post in every 6 feet. How many fence posts did he use?

A. 142 R4   **B. 143**   C. 143 R2   D. 153

14. Lilly estimated a quotient of 120 and found an actual quotient of 83. What should she do next? Explain.
Sample answer: She should check her estimate and check her quotient. The estimate tells her that the quotient is not reasonable, or she may have made a mistake on the estimate.

Also available in print

Enrichment Master

Name _____ Enrichment 10-7

Fact Path

Solve each problem by following the arrows. Write the final answer in the last box.

#	Start				End
1.	21	÷ 7	× 2	÷ 6	1
2.	54	÷ 6	÷ 3	× 5	15
3.	8	× 3	÷ 4	× 7	42
4.	5	÷ 5	× 9	× 4	36
5.	72	÷ 9	÷ 4	÷ 2	2
6.	6	× 2	÷ 4	× 6	18
7.	30	÷ 5	× 0	× 8	0
8.	8	× 3	÷ 6	× 5	9
9.	35	÷ 7	× 4	× 9	81
10.	4	× 7	− 3		5

Write two fact paths. Include a multiplication step and a division step in each path. **Check students' work.**

11.
12.

Also available in print

Problem Solving: Multiple-Step Problems

Domain
Number and Operations in Base Ten

Cluster
Use the four operations with whole numbers to solve problems.

Standards

4.OA.3 Solve multistep word problems posed with whole numbers and having whole-number answers using the four operations, including problems in which remainders must be interpreted. Represent these problems using equations with a letter standing for the unknown quantity. Assess the reasonableness of answers using mental computation and estimation strategies including rounding. Also **4.NBT.5**

Mathematical Practices

✔ Make sense of problems and persevere in solving them.

✔ Reason abstractly and quantitatively.

✔ Construct viable arguments and critique the reasoning of others.

✔ Model with mathematics.

○ Use appropriate tools strategically.

○ Attend to precision.

○ Look for and make use of structure.

○ Look for and express regularity in repeated reasoning.

 **Lesson Overview**

Objective	Essential Understanding	Vocabulary	Materials
Students will identify the hidden question in a multi-step problem. They use the answer to that hidden question to solve the original problem.	Some problems can be solved by first finding and solving a sub-problem(s) and then using that answer(s) to solve the original problem.		

 PROFESSIONAL DEVELOPMENT

Math Background

Sometimes more than one computational step is needed to solve a problem. Identifying such a problem requires careful reading in order to understand which operations are involved and in which order they should be performed. Many multi-step problems can be solved in more than one way, but for others there is only one correct sequence. To solve such problems, students need to apply logical reasoning.

In other instances multi-step problems can be solved by first identifying a sub-problem upon which the original problem is based. Once students identify and solve the sub-problem, they use the answer to solve the original problem.

1 Daily Common Core Review

Daily Common Core Review

Name _____

Daily Common Core Review **10-8**

1. Luis's family is going to the amusement park. Tickets cost $26 for each child. There are 7 children going. How much will all of their tickets cost?
   A $142
   B $162
   Ⓒ $182
   D $202

2. Traci wants to put the same number of books on each shelf on her bookcase. Which would be the quickest operation to use to figure out how many books go on each shelf?
   A Addition
   B Subtraction
   C Multiplication
   Ⓓ Division

3. Pedro collects baseball cards. He had 192. His friend Kevin gave him 267 more. His friend Shannon gave him 212 more. How many baseball cards does Pedro have now?
   A 771
   B 679
   Ⓒ 671
   D 579

4. Round the number 40,538 to the following places:
   Ten: __40,540__
   Hundred: __40,500__
   Thousand: __41,000__

5. Write the following number: seven hundred seventy-eight thousand, thirty-nine.
   __778,039__

6. **Mental Math** Warren planted 35 summer squash plants in 7 rows of his garden. How many summer squash plants were there in each row?
   __5 plants__

7. Jodie drove 4 hours to visit her grandmother. She averaged 60 miles per hour during her trip. How many miles did Jodie travel to see her grandmother?
   __240 miles__

Also available in print

Content Reviewed

Exercise 1   Multiplication
Exercise 2   Problem Solving
Exercise 3   Addition
Exercise 4   Rounding
Exercise 5   Write Numbers
Exercise 6   Division
Exercise 7   Multiplication

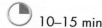 10–15 min **Problem-Based Interactive Learning**  Hands-On Minds-On

Overview Students will learn how to break a problem into steps before solving.

Focus What hidden questions lie within a multiple-step problem?

 **Engage**

Set the Purpose *Some problems can be solved by first finding and solving sub-problems, and then using that answer to help solve the original problem. Today, you will learn how identifying the hidden questions in a multiple-step problem can help you solve the problem.*

Connect *Tell about a time when you had to answer one question before you could answer another.* [Accept reasonable answers.]

MATHEMATICAL PRACTICES

Model with Mathematics
When students use number sentences to solve multiple-step problems, they are modeling with mathematics.

Pose the Problem *Susan has $45. She spends $15 on a book for her father, $20 on candles for her mother, and $6 on a board game for her brother. Does Susan have enough money left to buy a box of markers for $5?* Allow students time to explain their thinking and number sentences.

Whole-Class Discussion *What information are you given that you need to solve the problem?* [Price of the items bought; the amount of money she has] *What are you asked to find?* [Whether she can also buy a $5 item] *Decide what operation you need to use to solve this problem. Write a number sentence you can use to solve it. We can use the multiple-step problem-solving strategy to solve the problem.* Write $45 on the board. *How much money did Susan spend on gifts for her family? What operation can we use to find out?* [Add to find how much was spent: $15 + $20 + $6 = $41.] *What hidden question do you need to answer before you solve the question?* [How much money does Susan have left after she buys the gifts?] *What number sentence can we write to answer the hidden question?* [$45 − $41 = $4] *Is $4 enough to buy the box of markers?* [No]

Student Participation *Repeat the steps above using this problem. The scout group bought 20 T-shirts for $60 dollars. How much would it cost to buy 30 T-shirts from the same store?* [$90] *What hidden question do you need to answer first?* [How much does one T-shirt cost?]

book	$ 15.00
candles	$ 20.00
board game	$ 6.00
Total:	$ 41.00

Total	
book + candles + board game	$ 45
	− $ 41
Money left	
	$4

This is not enough money.

 Extend

Write a word problem that contains a hidden question.
[Answers will vary.]

Visual Learning

Problem Solving

Multiple-Step Problems

Justine and her father are going on a fishing trip. The prices for supplies, including tax, are shown in the table. Justine and her father have $25. They bought 2 box lunches, 2 bottles of water, 5 hooks, and 5 sinkers. How many pounds of bait can they buy?

Captain Bob's Price List	
Bait	$3 per pound
Hooks	60¢ each
Sinkers	40¢ each
Bottled water	$1 each
Box lunch	$6 each

How much money do Justine and her father have in all? [They have $25.] *How much does bait cost?* [$3 per pound]

Read & Understand

What do I know?	They bought: 2 lunches for $6 each 2 bottles of water for $1 each 5 hooks for 60¢ each 5 sinkers for 40¢ each
What am I asked to find?	The number of pounds of bait they can buy with the money they have left.

---

1 Visual Learning

Set the Purpose Call students' attention to the **Visual Learning Bridge** at the top of the page. *In this lesson, you will identify the hidden question needed to solve the original question in a multi-step problem.*

2 Guided Practice  MATHEMATICAL PRACTICES

Problem Solving Strategy *Use Reasoning* can be helpful to solve multi-step problems. To review this strategy refer students to the Student Handbook, p. xxiv.

Exercise 2
Error Intervention

If students are having difficulty identifying the hidden question,

then help them think through the information they have been given. *How many hours did Elsa work during the week?* [3] *At what rate?* [$10/hour] *What can you conclude about Elsa's earnings during the week?* [She earned $30 during the week.] *Using the same thought process, what can you conclude about Elsa's earnings over the weekend?* [Elsa earned $60 over the weekend.] Lead students to see that in order to answer the question "How much did Elsa earn last week?" they need to first answer a hidden question. How much did Elsa earn during the week and on the weekend?

Reteaching Have students identify the hidden question in the following problem: *Richard needs 14 feet of rope for a project. He buys a spool that has 175 inches of rope. Does he have enough rope?* [Yes; 14 ft × 12 = 168 in., 175 > 168] For another example and more practice, assign **Reteaching** Set H on p. 251.

3 Independent Practice  MATHEMATICAL PRACTICES

 Make Sense of Problems Remind students to name the hidden question in each exercise before solving the problem.

Lesson 10-8

Common Core

4.OA.3 Solve multistep word problems posed with whole numbers and having whole-number answers using the four operations, including problems in which remainders must be interpreted. Represent these problems using equations with a letter standing for the unknown quantity. Assess the reasonableness of answers using mental computation and estimation strategies including rounding. Also 4.NBT.5

Problem Solving

Multiple-Step Problems

Justine and her father are going on a fishing trip. The prices for supplies, including tax, are shown in the table. Justine and her father have $25. They bought 2 box lunches, 2 bottles of water, 5 hooks, and 5 sinkers. How many pounds of bait can they buy?

Captain Bob's Price List	
Bait	$3 per pound
Hooks	60¢ each
Sinkers	40¢ each
Bottled water	$1 each
Box lunch	$6 each

Guided Practice* MATHEMATICAL PRACTICES

Do you know HOW?

Solve.

1. Elsa babysits for the Smyth family. She earns $10 per hour on weekdays. She earns $15 per hour on the weekend. Last week, she worked 3 hours during the week and 4 hours on the weekend. How much did Elsa earn last week? $90

Do you UNDERSTAND?

2. What is the hidden question or questions in Problem 1? See margin.

 3. **Write a Problem** Write a problem that contains a hidden question. Check students' answers.

Independent Practice MATHEMATICAL PRACTICES

 Persevere Write the answer to the hidden question or questions. Then solve the problem. Write your answer in a complete sentence.

4. Gabriella buys lunch for herself and her friend. She buys 2 sandwiches and 2 drinks. Each sandwich costs $4. Each drink costs $1.50. How much did Gabriella spend on lunch? $11

5. Jamie is buying bowls for a school ice cream social. She buys 5 packages of red bowls, 3 packages of orange bowls, 4 packages of green bowls, and 7 packages of white bowls. Each package contains 8 bowls. How many bowls did she buy in all? 152 bowls

Applying Math Practices

- What am I asked to find?
- What else can I try?
- How are quantities related?
- How can I explain my work?
- How can I use math to model the problem?
- Can I use tools to help?
- Is my work precise?
- Why does this work?
- How can I generalize?

246 *For another example, see Set H on page 251.*

---

2. How much did Elsa earn during the week? How much did Elsa earn on the weekend?

How much money have Justine and her father spent so far? [$19]

Plan

Find the hidden question. How much money do Justine and her father have left?

The cost of lunches is	2 × $6	= $12
The cost of water is	2 × $1	= $2
The cost of hooks is	5 × 60¢	= $3
The cost of sinkers is	5 × 40¢	= $2
	The total is	$19

$25 − $19 = $6   They have $6 left.

Divide to find how many pounds of bait they can buy.

6 ÷ 3 = 2   They can buy 2 pounds of bait.

If Justine and her father have $6 left, why can they only buy 2 pounds of bait? [Each pound of bait costs $3. $6 is enough money to purchase 2 pounds of bait.]

Read & Understand

What do know?

They bought:

2 lunches for $6 each
2 bottles of water for $1 each
5 hooks for 60¢ each
5 sinkers for 40¢ each

What am asked to find?

The number of pounds of bait they can buy with the money they have left

Plan

Find the hidden question. How much money do Justine and her father have left?

The cost of lunches is	2 × $6	= $12
The cost of water is	2 × $1	= $2
The cost of hooks is	5 × 60¢	= $3
The cost of sinkers is	5 × 40¢	= $2
	The total is	$19

$25 − $19 = $6   They have $6 left.

Divide to find how many pounds of bait they can buy.

6 ÷ 3 = 2   They can buy 2 pounds of bait.

---

6. Kelly used 6 cups of apples, 4 cups of oranges, and 2 cups of grapes to make a fruit salad. She put an equal amount in each of 6 bowls. How many cups of fruit salad were in each bowl?
2 cups

Use the data at the right for **8** through **11**.

8. The band needs to purchase 60 T-shirts. How much would it cost to purchase them from Shirt Shack?
$540

9. How much would it cost the band to purchase 60 T-shirts from Just Jerseys?
$600

10. **Reason** How much more would it cost to buy 24 T-shirts at Just Jerseys than at Shirt Shack?
$24

11. **Construct Arguments** Would it be less expensive to buy one shirt from Just Jerseys or Shirt Shack? Explain.
Shirt Shack; $90 ÷ 10 = $9

12. **Model** Each football practice is 45 minutes long. The team's next game is 6 practices away. How many minutes will they practice before the game?

A 135 minutes   **C** 243 minutes

B 270 minutes   **D** 2,430 minutes

7. Muriel used the same recipe as Kelly to make her fruit salad. Muriel also added 1 cup of cherries and 1 cup of bananas. She put 2 cups of fruit salad into each bowl. How many bowls did Muriel need?
7 bowls

Shirt Shack	
Number of shirts	Price
10	$90
20	$180
50	$450

Just Jerseys	
Number of shirts	Price
8	$80
24	$240
48	$480

? minutes in all

45	45	45	45	45	45

↑
length of each practice

Students use underlying processes and mathematical tools for Exercises 4–12. Remind students to use estimation or inverse operations to check for reasonableness when solving each problem.

Exercise 11

© **Construct Arguments** Make sure students are able to present a logical argument. Ask them how they would compare the price of one shirt from each store.

Exercise 12

© **Model with Mathematics** If students are having trouble, encourage them to write a number sentence to make the problem easier. *The team practices for 45 minutes 6 times before their next game. How can this be expressed as addition?* [45 + 45 + 45 + 45 + 45 + 45 = 270] *How can this be expressed as multiplication?* [6 × 45 = 270]

Early Finishers Have students write their own word problems with hidden questions.

Close

Essential Understanding Some problems can be solved by first finding and solving a sub-problem(s) and then using that answer(s) to solve the original problem. *In this lesson, you learned to identify the hidden question in a multiple-step problem.*

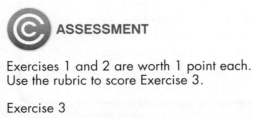 **ASSESSMENT**

Exercises 1 and 2 are worth 1 point each.
Use the rubric to score Exercise 3.

Exercise 3

Writing to Explain Students should be able to identify the hidden question in a multiple-step problem.

ELL Model Thinking Aloud For students who need additional writing support, suggest they talk out the problem so they can identify the hidden question. What do you need to know to find out how much change Sheila received? _____ [The amount of money she paid] How can you find out how much Sheila paid? _____ [By finding the total cost of the fruit]

Student Samples
3-point answer The student correctly identifies the hidden question and shows a good understanding of the material.

2-point answer The student is unable to find the hidden question but shows some understanding of the material.

1-point answer The student shows no understanding of the material.

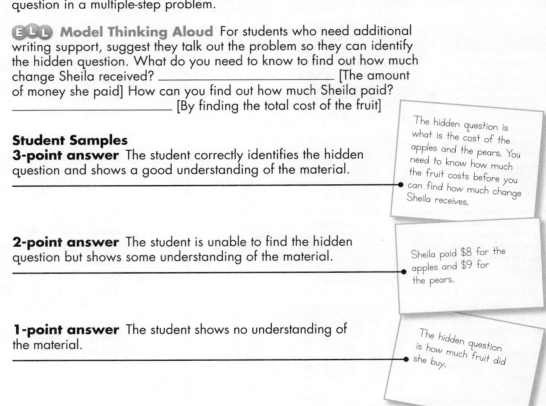

> The hidden question is what is the cost of the apples and the pears. You need to know how much the fruit costs before you can find how much change Sheila receives.

> Sheila paid $8 for the apples and $9 for the pears.

> The hidden question is how much fruit did she buy.

Quick Check Master

Name _____ Quick Check **10-8**

1. Zoe's recipe calls for 1 pound of walnuts. She has 4 pounds of walnuts. How many extra pounds of walnuts does Zoe have?
   A 1 pound
   B 2 pounds
   (C) 3 pounds
   D 4 pounds

2. Jorge wants to buy carpet for his living room and bedroom. His living room is 30 square yards and his bedroom is 21 square yards. If carpet costs $12 a square yard, how much will it cost to carpet these rooms?
   (A) $612
   B $562
   C $360
   D $252

3. **Writing to Explain** Find the hidden question in the problem below and explain why it's the hidden question.
   Sheila bought four bags of apples and three bags of pears from the market. Each bag of apples cost $2 and each bag of pears cost $3. She paid with a twenty dollar bill. How much change did she receive?
   See students' samples to the right.

 **Formative** Assessment

Use the **Quick Check** to assess students' understanding.

Prescription for Differentiated Instruction
Use student work on the **Quick Check** to prescribe differentiated instruction.

Points	Prescription
0–2	Intervention
3–4	On-Level
5	Advanced

Differentiated Instruction

Intervention

Multiple-Step Problems

 10–15 min

- Write the problem from the Quick Check on the board.

- Have students work in groups to solve the problem. Have one member of the group write out the steps they took to solve the problem.

- Ask students: *What information did you have to find to solve this problem?*

On-Level

Practice | **Center Activity**

Teamwork

Get Started ↟↟ or ↟↟ Get paper and a pencil.
Put 1 2 3 4 in a bag.

Repeat for Each Round Take turns reading the items available, and the prices of those items, at the bicycle rental shop. Choose **a**, **b**, or **c**. Pick a tile. Pick two tiles if your group has only two students. Do the jobs listed below in order. To find your job, find the number that matches the tile you chose.

1. Read the problem.
   Tell your group what you know and what you are asked to find.
2. Tell your group what one of the hidden questions is.
   Explain how to answer that question.
3. Tell your group about a second hidden question.
   Explain how to answer that question.
4. Explain how to solve the problem using the answers to the hidden questions.

a. The Adams family rented 3 bicycles for adults and 2 children's bicycles for half a day. They paid with four $20-bills. How much change did they get?

b. Carl paid for his family's accessories. He rented 5 helmets and 5 locks. How much did Carl spend on accessories?

c. The Johnson family rented 2 adult bicycles and two baby seats for a day. What did the Johnson family spend at the bicycle rental shop?

Bicycle Billy's Best Buys

Adult Bicycle		Accessories	
Full Day	$27	Baby seat	$15
Half Day	$15	Helmet	$5
Child's Bicycle		Lock	$3
Full Day	$20	Hand Pump	$2
Half Day	$12	Water	$1.50

If you have more time Create your own list of what you would like to get from the bike shop. How much would it cost?

Center Activity ★ 10-8

Advanced

Practice | **Center Activity**

Teamwork

Get Started ↟↟ or ↟↟ Get paper and a pencil.
Put 1 2 3 4 in a bag.
Take turns reading the items available and the prices for those items at the bicycle rental shop.

Repeat for Each Round Choose **a**, **b**, or **c**. Ask one group member to read the problem aloud. Discuss what you know, and what you have to find. Pick a tile. Pick two tiles if your group has only two students. Do the jobs listed below in order. To find your job, find the number that matches the tile you chose.

1. Ask one of the hidden questions.
   Explain how to answer that question.
2. Ask a second hidden question.
   Explain how to answer that question.
3. Ask a third hidden question.
   Explain how to answer that question.
4. Explain how to solve the problem using the answers to the three hidden questions.

Spinning Wheels Bike Shop

Adult's Bicycle	$35	Helmet	$5.00
Child's Bicycle	$18	Lock	$3.00
Baby Seat	$15	Gloves	$1.50
Bicycle Built for Two	$45	Hand Pump	$2.50

a. How much would it cost a family to rent 2 bicycles for adults, 2 bicycles for children and 2 baby seats?

b. Jo paid for the accessories for her family. She rented 4 helmets, 4 locks and 4 pairs of gloves. How much did Jo spend on accessories?

c. A family has $85 to spend at the bicycle shop. They rent a child's bike, a bicycle built for two and 3 helmets. What can they rent with the money they have left?

If you have more time Create your own list of what you would like to get from the bike shop. How much would it cost?

Center Activity ★★ 10-8

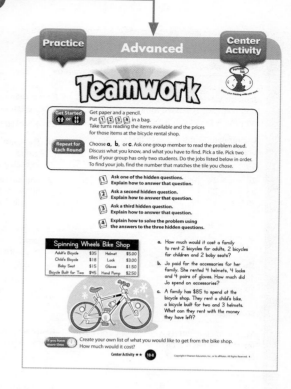

ELL Partner Talk Listen for questions being posed and answered, followed by interpretations of those answers to solve a problem.

Leveled Homework

Reteaching Master

Name _____

Problem Solving: Multiple-Step Problems

Reteaching 10-8

Solve Problems Step-by-Step

Scott and Gina want to go see a movie after they eat dinner. They have brought $35 with them. Scott's meal costs $9 and Gina's meal costs $8. Movie tickets are $9 each. Will they have enough money left over after dinner to pay for 2 movie tickets?

First Step
Write down what you know:
- They have $35 to spend.
- They are spending $9 and $8 on dinner.

Second Step
Write down what you need to know:
- How much money is left over?
- Is it enough for 2 movie tickets?

Third Step
Develop a problem-solving strategy:
- Subtract $9 and $8 from $35.
(Tip: Instead of subtracting these from $35 one at a time, combine them and then subtract from $35.)

```
  $ 9          $35
+ $ 8   then, −$17
 $17.00        $18
```

Fourth Step
Finish the problem:
- Is $18 enough for 2 movie tickets that cost $9 each?
$9 × 2 = $18
They have $18 left. Yes, they have enough for 2 movie tickets.

Solve the problems below using the step-by-step process.

1. Nick and his friends are working on a project. They need to write 29 pages altogether. If his friend Kara writes 14 pages, and his friend Jared writes 12 pages, how many pages are left for Nick to write? **3 pages**

2. Ashlyn and Brooke went to the arcade with $18. They bought 4 bottles of water, which cost $2 each. They each bought a sticker book for $3 each. Ashlyn put $1 in a fundraiser jar. A game of pool cost $3 per game. Did they have enough money left to play? **Yes**

3. **Reasoning** Cyndi and Jewel were shopping for school supplies. They had $14 to spend. They spent $4 on pencils, $3 on pens, and $6 on notebook paper. Cyndi thought she had enough money left over to buy a $2 pencil sharpener. Was she correct? **No. She would need $1 more.**

R 10-8

Also available in print

Practice Master

Name _____

Problem Solving: Multiple-Step Problems

Practice 10-8

Write and answer the hidden question or questions. Then solve the problem. Write your answer in a complete sentence.

County Fair Admission	
Adults	$5
Students	$3
Children	$2

1. Mario and his family went to the county fair. They bought 2 adult passes and 3 children's passes. What was the total cost for the family? **How much was the total of the adult passes? $10; How much was the total of the children's passes? $6; The total for Mario's family was $16.**

2. A bus has 12 rows with 1 seat in each row on one side and 12 rows with 2 seats in each row on the other side. How many seats does the bus have altogether? **How many seats are on the first side? 12 seats; How many seats are on the second side? 24 seats; The total number of seats on the bus is 36.**

3. **Writing to Explain** Write a problem about going to the laundromat that has a hidden question. A single load of laundry costs $2 and a double load costs $4. Solve your problem. **Check students' problems.**

P 10-8

Also available in print

Enrichment Master

Name _____

Car Wash Day

Enrichment 10-8

Solve each exercise and show your work.

1. The school held a Car Wash Day. It ran from 10 A.M. to 4 P.M. Twelve students were needed each hour. How many students were needed for the whole day? **10 A.M. to 4 P.M. = 6 hours; 6 × 12 = 72 students**

2. The students washed 12 cars in the first hour, 15 cars in the second hour, and 10 cars in each of the next 4 hours. How many cars did they wash in all? **12 + 15 + (4 × 10) = 67 cars**

3. Look back at Exercise 2. The students earned $60 in the first hour and $50 in the third hour. What do you think they earned in the fourth hour? Explain. **$50; They washed the same number of cars in the third and fourth hours.**

4. One group of 12 students worked in teams, with the same number of students on each team. In what different ways might the teams have been formed? **3 teams of 4 students each, 4 teams of 3 students each, 2 teams of 6 students each, or 6 teams of 2 students each.**

5. If each car owner paid $5.99 per wash, about how much did the school earn during Car Wash Day? (Hint: Look back at Exercise 2 to see how many cars were washed.) **About $6 × 70 = $420**

E 10-8

Also available in print

 DIGITAL eTools **Place-Value Blocks** www.pearsonsuccessnet.com

 DIGITAL eTools **Place-Value Blocks** www.pearsonsuccessnet.com

 DIGITAL eTools **Place-Value Blocks** www.pearsonsuccessnet.com

Topic 10
Reteaching

Set A, pages 228–229

James is placing 4 photos on each page of a photo album. If he has a total of 32 photos, how many pages can James fill?

Use repeated subtraction to find the number of pages.

$$32 - 4 = 28$$
$$28 - 4 = 24$$
$$24 - 4 = 20$$
$$20 - 4 = 16$$
$$16 - 4 = 12$$
$$12 - 4 = 8$$
$$8 - 4 = 4$$
$$4 - 4 = 0$$

Subtract 4 eight times.

There are eight groups of 4 in 32.
$$32 \div 4 = 8$$
So, James can fill 8 pages.

Remember you can think about repeated subtraction to divide.

Use repeated subtraction to divide.

1. There are 24 students in 8 equal groups. How many students are in each group? **3 students**

2. The hockey club has 35 hockey sticks for all the teams to share equally. If each team gets 5 hockey sticks, how many teams are there? **7 teams**

3. A chef uses 2 large eggs for each omelet. How many omelets are made if a total of 20 eggs are used? **10 omelets**

4. A collection of 45 stickers is shared among 5 friends. How any stickers does each friend receive? **9 stickers**

Set B, pages 230–231

Mary is mailing letters with 2 stamps on each letter. If she has a total of 30 stamps, how many letters can Mary send?

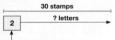

30 stamps
 2 | ? letters

Stamps on each letter

Use repeated subtraction to find the number of letters.

$$30 \div 2$$

30	Estimate: How many 2s are in 30? Try 10.
−20	Multiply 10 × 2 and subtract.
10	Estimate: How many 2s are in 10? Use 5.
−10	Multiply 5 × 2 and subtract.
0	

$$10 + 5 = 15$$ There are 15 2s in 30.

Mary can mail a total of 15 letters.

Remember you can think about sharing equally to divide.

Use the diagram to help you divide.

1. There are 15 chairs in 3 equal groups. How many chairs are in each group? **5 chairs**

15 chairs
| ? | ? | ? |

2. The soccer club has 28 balls for all the teams to share equally. If each team gets 7 balls, how many teams are there? **4 teams**

28 balls
| 7 | ? teams

Balls for each team

Set C, pages 232–234

Tom divides 54 pennies equally among 4 stacks. How many pennies are in each stack? How many are left over?

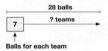
Use place-value blocks.

Each stack has 13 pennies.
Two pennies are left over.

Remember to divide the tens and then the ones.

Divide. You may use place-value blocks or pictures to help.
1–10 See margin.

| 1. 38 CDs | 2. 42 nickels |
| 5 stacks | 3 stacks |

| 3. 62 dimes | 4. 77 nickels |
| 4 stacks | 6 stacks |

| 5. 53 stickers | 6. 46 quarters |
| 8 stacks | 5 stacks |

| 7. 65 marbles | 8. 81 pennies |
| 9 piles | 9 stacks |

| 9. 55 pencils | 10. 75 pens |
| 6 stacks | 8 piles |

Set D, pages 236–238

Find $67 \div 4$.

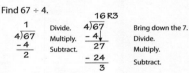

	1	Divide.		16 R3		Bring down the 7.
4)67		Multiply.	4)67			Divide.
−4		Subtract.	−4			Multiply.
2			27			Subtract.
			−24			
			3			

Check:
$$\begin{array}{r} 2 \\ 16 \\ \times\ 4 \\ \hline 64 \end{array} \qquad \begin{array}{r} 64 \\ +\ 3 \\ \hline 67 \end{array} \qquad \text{The answer checks.}$$

Remember that the remainder must be less than the divisor.

Divide. Check your answer.

1. $43 \div 7$	2. $33 \div 2$
6 R1	16 R1
3. $19 \div 5$	4. $53 \div 2$
3 R4	26 R1
5. $86 \div 7$	6. $85 \div 3$
12 R2	28 R1
7. $94 \div 4$	8. $47 \div 3$
23 R2	15 R2
9. $46 \div 3$	10. $59 \div 4$
15 R1	14 R3
11. $88 \div 7$	12. $83 \div 5$
12 R4	16 R3

Purpose

- Provide students with more examples and practice for each lesson in the topic.

- For intervention materials, use the resources listed in the chart on the next page.

Set C

1. 7 CDs, 3 left over
2. 14 nickels, 0 left over
3. 15 dimes, 2 left over
4. 12 nickels, 5 left over
5. 6 stickers, 5 left over
6. 9 quarters, 1 left over
7. 7 marbles, 2 left over
8. 9 pennies, 0 left over
9. 9 pencils, 1 left over
10. 9 pens, 3 left over

Response to Intervention

RTI   **Ongoing Intervention**

TIER 1   ONGOING

- Lessons with guiding questions to assess understanding
- Support to prevent misconceptions and to reteach

RTI   **Strategic Intervention**

TIER 2   STRATEGIC

- Targeted to small groups who need more support
- Easy to implement

RTI   **Intensive Intervention**

TIER 3   INTENSIVE

- Instruction to accelerate progress
- Instruction focused on foundational skills

 Item Analysis for Diagnosis and Intervention

Objective	© Common Core Standards	Exercises	Student Book Lessons	Intervention System
Use repeated subtraction to model division.	4.NBT.6	Set A, 1–4	10-1	G35
Record division as repeated subtraction	4.NBT.6	Set B, 1–2	10-2	G35
Use place value to understand the algorithm of long division.	4.NBT.6	Set C, 1–10	10-3	G53
Use the standard algorithm to divide 2-digit by 1-digit numbers.	4.NBT.6	Set D, 1–12	10-4	G54

Topic 10
Reteaching
INTERVENTION

Set E, pages 240–241

Find 915 ÷ 6.

Estimate: 900 ÷ 6 = 150

The estimate is more than 100, so you can start dividing the hundreds.

```
     152 R3
  6)915
   - 6            Divide the hundreds.
     31
   - 30           Divide the tens.
     15
   - 12           Divide the ones.
      3           Include the remainder.
```

Remember to use an estimate to double-check your answers.

Divide. Check your answer.

1. 448 ÷ 4   2. 651 ÷ 5
   112   130 R1
3. 398 ÷ 3   4. 365 ÷ 3
   132 R2   121 R2
5. 437 ÷ 2   6. 863 ÷ 4
   218 R1   215 R3
7. 7)710   8. 5)572
   101 R3   114 R2
9. 6)618   10. 7)814
   103   116 R2
11. 5)962   12. 2)735
    192 R2   367 R1
13. 3)622   14. 8)839
    207 R1   104 R7
15. 4)506   16. 9)926
    126 R2   102 R8
17. 5)841   18. 8)910
    168 R1   113 R6

Set F, pages 242–243

Find 566 ÷ 6.

```
     94 R2
  6)566
   - 0       There are not enough
     56      hundreds to divide.
   - 54      Regroup the hundreds
     26      as tens and divide.
   - 24      Bring down the ones
      2      and divide.
```

Remember to estimate the quotient to help you decide where to start dividing. Then divide.

Tell whether you will start dividing at the hundreds or the tens.

1. 710 ÷ 9   2. 601 ÷ 5
   Tens; 78 R8   Hundreds; 120 R1
3. 398 ÷ 8   4. 429 ÷ 2
   Tens; 49 R6   Hundreds; 214 R1
5. 628 ÷ 3   6. 255 ÷ 4
   Hundreds; 209 R1   Tens; 63 R3
7. 470 ÷ 6   8. 739 ÷ 7
   Tens; 78 R2   Hundreds; 105 R4
9. 409 ÷ 5   10. 110 ÷ 3
   Tens; 81 R4   Tens; 36 R2
11. 603 ÷ 4   12. 727 ÷ 9
    Hundreds; 150 R3   Tens; 80 R7

Set G, pages 244–245

Find 4,849 ÷ 4. Estimate first. 4,800 ÷ 4 = 1,200.

```
    1,212 R1      Check:  1,212
  4)4,849               ×     4
   - 4                   4,848
     08                +     1
    - 8                  4,849
     04
    - 4         The quotient 1,212 R1 is
     09         close to the estimate,
    - 8         1,200.
      1
```

Remember that you can use your estimate to check that your answer is reasonable.

Divide.

1. 7,206 ÷ 6   2. 661 ÷ 3
   1,201   220 R1
3. 4)424   4. 3)9,143
   106   3,047 R2
5. 1,255 ÷ 3   6. 411 ÷ 8
   418 R1   51 R3
7. 4)542   8. 6)9,232
   135 R2   1,538 R4

Set H, pages 246–247

Answer the hidden question first. Then solve the problem.

Brett and his family spent $21 for admission to the county fair. They bought 2 adult passes for $6 each and 3 children's passes for $3 each. How much more money did Brett's family spend on adult passes than children's passes?

$6 × 2 = $12 → Price of adult passes

$3 × 3 = $9 → Price of children's passes

Brett's family spent $12 on adult passes and $9 on children passes.

Use the hidden question to solve the problem.

How much more money did Brett's family spend on adult passes than children passes?

$12 − $9 = $3

Brett's family spent $3 more on adult passes.

Remember to find a hidden question to help you solve the problem.

1. Angelique works at a store at the mall. She earns a wage of $8 an hour and earns $10 an hour if she works on weekends and holidays. Last week, she worked 24 hours during the week and 16 hours during the weekend. How much did Angelique earn last week?
   $352
2. Brendan takes violin and guitar lessons. Each day, he practices 40 minutes on the violin and 25 minutes on the guitar. How many minutes does he practice his instruments in 5 days?
   325 minutes

Purpose

- Provide students with more examples and practice for each lesson in the topic.

- For intervention materials, use the resources listed in the chart on the next page.

Response to Intervention

RTI **Ongoing Intervention**
TIER 1 ONGOING
- Lessons with guiding questions to assess understanding
- Support to prevent misconceptions and to reteach

RTI **Strategic Intervention**
TIER 2 STRATEGIC
- Targeted to small groups who need more support
- Easy to implement

RTI **Intensive Intervention**
TIER 3 INTENSIVE

- Instruction to accelerate progress
- Instruction focused on foundational skills

Item Analysis for Diagnosis and Intervention

Objective	© Common Core Standards	Exercises	Student Book Lessons	Intervention System
Use the standard algorithm to divide 3-digit by 1-digit numbers.	**4.NBT.6**	Set E, 1–18	10-5	G55, G56
Use the standard algorithm to divide 3-digit numbers by 1-digit numbers and properly decide where to begin dividing.	**4.NBT.6**	Set F, 1–12	10-6	
Estimate and find quotients for 4-digit dividends and 1-digit divisors.	**4.NBT.6**	Set G, 1–8	10-7	G55, G56, G58
Identify the hidden question in a multi-step problem. Then use the answer to that hidden question to solve the original problem.	**4.OA.3**	Set H, 1–2	10-8	J3, J4

Developing Fluency: Dividing by 1-Digit Divisors
TOPIC TEST

Topic 10
Test

© ASSESSMENT

Multiple Choice

1. Three friends have 39 water balloons to share equally. How many water balloons will each friend get? (10-1)

   A 9

   B 12

   C 13

   D 15

2. For the division problem 589 ÷ 4, in what place will you start dividing? (10-6)

   A thousands

   B hundreds

   C tens

   D ones

3. Two boxes contain a total of 576 pencils. If each box has the same number of pencils, how many pencils are in each box? (10-5)

   A 1,152

   B 328

   C 288

   D 238

4. Tia has 15 metamorphic, 8 igneous, and 7 sedimentary rocks. She displays her rocks equally in 2 cases. Which shows how she found the number of rocks to put in each case? (10-8)

   A 2 × 16

   B 16 ÷ 2

   C 2 × 30

   D 30 ÷ 2

5. Nelly has 74 bricks to outline 5 different flower beds. How many bricks will she use for each flower bed if she uses the same number around each? (10-3)

   A Each flower bed will use 10 bricks. There will be 4 left over.

   B Each flower bed will use 13 bricks. There will be 9 left over.

   C Each flower bed will use 14 bricks. There will be 0 left over.

   D Each flower bed will use 14 bricks. There will be 4 left over.

6. What is 318 ÷ 4? (10-5)

   A 78 R2

   B 78

   C 79 R2

   D 79

7. Harold earned $1,468 by mowing lawns for 3 months in the summer. Which number sentence shows the best way to estimate the amount he earned for each month? (10-7)

   A $1,500 ÷ 3 = $500

   B $1,500 ÷ 5 = $300

   C $2,000 ÷ 5 = $400

   D 3 × $1,500 = $4,500

Constructed Response

8. Mason bought a package of 20 wheels. Each model car needs 4 wheels. How many cars can he make? (10-2) **5**

   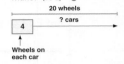
   Wheels on each car

9. Each costume requires 2 yards of material. How many costumes can Sara make out of 35 yards? How much material will she have left? (10-4) **17 costumes; 1 yard left**

10. Tammy bought 24 apples to feed her horse. She wants to give her horse 2 apples a day. Tammy said that after 10 days she will have 4 apples left. Is Tammy correct? Explain your thinking. (10-2) **See margin.**

11. A biologist banded 3 birds in a week. If the biologist bands the same number of birds each week, how many weeks will it take her to band 42 birds? Use repeated subtraction. (10-1) **14 weeks**

12. Ken has 78 pieces of wood for building birdhouses. Each birdhouse needs 6 pieces of wood. How many birdhouses can Ken make? (10-3)
   13 birdhouses
   ||||||||||||||

13. A baker made 52 rolls. He put an equal amount in each of the 4 baskets in the display case. How many rolls did he put in each basket? (10-4) **13 rolls**

14. Can you tell the number of digits that will be in the quotient for 427 ÷ 7 just by looking at the problem? Explain. (10-6)
   See margin.

15. A school has $1,016 for scholarships. The money was awarded equally to 8 students. Find the amount of money each student received. Show all of your work. (10-7) **$127**

16. Keith does work for his neighbors. When he does work outdoors he earns $12 an hour. When he works indoors he earns $8 an hour. Last month he did 18 hours of work outdoors and 16 hours of work indoors. How much did Keith earn last month? (10-8) **$344**

17. Tracey has 452 trading cards. She wants to put an equal number into each of 3 books to display them. How many cards will there be in each book? How many will be left over? (10-5)
   150 cards; 2 cards left over

18. There are 8,960 people who live in Springdale. The town is separated into 5 voting areas that each have the same number of people. How many people live in each voting area? (10-7)
   1,792 people

Topic 10 Test

Purpose

- Assess students' understanding of the concepts and skills in Topic 10 using multiple-choice and constructed response formats.

- Additional assessment options can be found in the Teacher Resource Masters.

- For intervention materials that correspond to all tests, use the resources listed in the chart on the next page.

10. Yes after 10 days she will have fed the horse 2 × 10 = 20 apples. There will be 4 apples left to feed the horse.

14. Yes. It will have a two-digit quotient, because 4 cannot be divided by 7 but 42 can.

Test-Taking Tips

Discuss with students the following tips for test success.

Understand the Question
- Look for important words.
- Turn the question into a statement: "I need to find out…"

Gather Information
- Get information from text.
- Get information from pictures, maps, diagrams, tables, and graphs.

Make a Plan
- Think about problem-solving skills and strategies.
- Choose computation methods.

Make Smart Choices
- Eliminate wrong answers.
- Try working backward from an answer.
- Check answers for reasonableness; estimate.

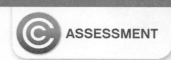

RTI

Item Analysis for Diagnosis and Intervention

Objective	Common Core Standards	Test Items	Student Book Lessons	Intervention System
Use repeated subtraction to model division.	4.NBT.6	1, 11	10-1	G35
Record division as repeated subtraction.	4.NBT.6	8, 10	10-2	G35
Use place value to understand the algorithm of long division.	4.NBT.6	5, 12	10-3	G53
Use the standard algorithm to divide 2-digit by 1-digit numbers.	4.NBT.6	9, 13	10-4	G54
Use the standard algorithm to divide 3-digit by 1-digit numbers.	4.NBT.6	3, 6, 17	10-5	G55, 56
Use the standard algorithm to divide 3-digit numbers by 1-digit numbers and properly decide where to begin dividing.	4.NBT.6	2, 14	10-6	G46
Estimate and find quotients for 4-digit dividends and 1-digit divisors.	4.NBT.6	7, 15, 18	10-7	G55, G56, G58
Identify the hidden question in a multi-step problem. Then use the answer to that hidden question to solve the original problem.	4.OA.3	4, 16	10-8	J3, J4

Alternate Test Master

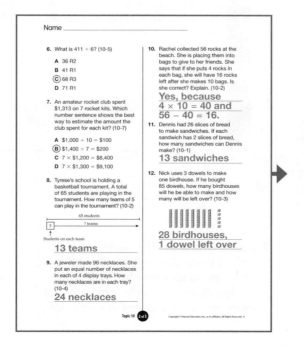

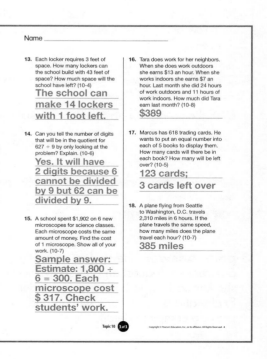

Teacher Resource Masters, Topic 10

253

 ASSESSMENT

Purpose Assess students' understanding of the concepts and skills in Topic 10 through a performance-based task.

Task For this assessment, students divide two-digit and three-digit numbers by one-digit numbers.

Get Ready Discuss arrays. Review division facts with students.

Guiding the Activity Help students connect the remainders in the division to the poetry displays. If needed, use concrete models to show that the remaining poems would be displayed in an additional row.

Questioning Strategies What answer do you get when you divide 45 by 2? Where would those remaining poems be displayed?

If you divide by 5 and have a remainder, can that be one of your display options?

What operations are needed when deciding how to display the poems of both classes together?

Sample student work:

> 1. No, because 45 cannot be divided by 2 evenly; 45 ÷ 2 = 22 R1.
>
> 2. There can be 3 rows of 15 poems each or 5 rows with 9 poems each.
>
> 3. There would be 21 poems in each of 3 rows because 63 ÷ 3 = 21.
>
> 4. There would be 3 rows of 21 poems OR 1 row of 31 poems and 1 row of 32 poems.
>
> 5. There would be 108 poems total. They could have 2 rows of 54, 3 rows of 36, or 4 rows of 27 poems.
>
> 6. If the poems are arranged in 7 equal rows of 26 poems, then 2 poems will be left over. All of the poems can be displayed in 8 equal rows of 23 poems.

The fourth-grade students at Skyview Elementary are studying poetry. They are trying to decide how to display their poems in the hallway. They want to put the poems in at least 2 rows, but not more than 5 rows.

| Mr. Chang's class | Mrs. Steele's class |
| 45 Poems | 63 Poems |

See margin for 1–6.

1. Mr. Chang's class wrote 45 poems. Can the students put the same number of poems in each row if they use 2 rows? Explain.

2. Describe two different ways that the students in Mr. Chang's class can display their 45 poems. For each display, tell how many poems would be in each row. There can be one row with fewer poems than the rest.

3. Mrs. Steele's class wrote 63 poems. How many poems would be in each row if the students use 3 rows? Explain.

4. Describe two different ways that the students in Mrs. Steele's class can display their 63 poems. For each display, tell how many poems would be in each row. There can be one row with fewer poems than the rest.

5. If both Mr. Chang's and Mrs. Steele's classes display their poems together, how might they be displayed? Describe two different ways.

6. The fourth-grade students ask all the students of Skyview Elementary to write one poem. If they collect 184 poems, can all of the poems be displayed in 7 equal rows? Can all of them be displayed in 8 equal rows? Explain.

 254 Topic 10

Scoring Rubric

3-point answer The student correctly answers each question and shows he or she knows how to interpret remainders. Explanations are clearly written and provide complete detail.

2-point answer The student shows limited understanding of divisibility rules and how to interpret the remainders. Explanations are fairly complete, but there are several errors in computations.

1-point answer The student shows little or no understanding of divisibility rules and how to interpret the remainders. Explanations are missing or incomplete and there are many computational errors.